THE BOOK OF
BURIED LETTERS

**a real-life journey of
insight and intuition**

MAREN MEANDERING

the book of buried letters

A Real-Life Journey of Insight and Intuition

Is it possible to create the future between pen and paper? And then live in the world figmented by imagination?

- age 13

THE BOOK OF BURIED LETTERS

Copyright © 2016 by Maren Meandering

Publisher's note: This is a work based on non-fiction.

Printed in the United States of America

Edited, formatted, and interior design by Maren Meandering

Cover art design by Maren Meandering

Meandering, Maren

The Book of Buried Letters / Maren

p. cm.

ISBN-13: 978-1-7321128-0-3

First edition published 2018

10 9 8 7 6 5 4 3 2 1 0

It starts with a special thanks to Hyouw, secret keeper of the chocolate underground, May Day flowers, and treasure hunts. King Grassy Grass and Scandium, and Teleporter Bird, Longneck Bird, Black Bird, Daisy Squirrel, Kitty, and Pígœñ. Woven into the very fibers of it all, the guardian of our worlds, the builder of trebuchets and great bonfires, you will never be forgotten and are loved eternally.

Table of Contents

Chapter One

Memory

There is nothing quite like a treasure hunt. Especially when it opens a story. There once was a four-year-old girl who emptied a large glass jar of buttons, examining them one by one. She placed them in piles, guessed which were the oldest and pressed her fingers hard to imprint the holes upon her skin. Then she gathered them in scoops and filled her mother's sewing basket. After which, the jar accompanied her to a grove of pines where her hands dug just deep enough in the dirt to bury it.

"There." She said placing a letter in the glass and tightening the lid.

For most people, memories begin formalization around three or four years old. Scientists, on the whole, state any earlier claims memory can't truly be substantiated. There are several reasons they give. Some say infants from birth to about four do not have the mental capacity for a kind of autobiographical recollection or memory storage in the first person.

Some specialists studying memory and the brain say other animals also show signs of infantile amnesia. Maybe the amnesia is caused by the rapid development of brain cells which essentially gets rid of unusable information while retaining essential information that helps with survival. According to a study, this is because new neurons disrupt older formatted brain circuits. To support this idea scientists slowed neurogenesis in baby mice and found that by doing this they could force memories to last longer.

Could it be possible then for memory to extend beyond the regular infantile amnesia? Is it possible for someone to have their brain function in a meditative state which doesn't necessarily slow development in a way that is detrimental, but in a way that alters one's view of the world?

Between bouts of screaming from colic, the little girl said she, "fell into the air... like being the birds' songs and I moved as a dust fleck floating in the sun's rays." Essentially, she meditated right from the start. She mimicked the hum of the car in deep breaths of "hommmmm." It settled her. It vibrated an echoing harmony between her mind, ears, and heart. And she remembered. Her mind had a way of altering traditionally formed memories. She moved into life not about it. In order not to feel wind stinging upon her skin, she says her spirit ran with it. It held onto the wings of bees, and the sway of the clover, and felt of the car upon the pavement. She held onto being wrapped in arms. The feel of the rubber nipples of the bottle as her mouth search for the position. She remembered the touch of hands, and what it felt like to be carried or placed down, a sense of altitude shift. She listened to the beat of her heart and the expansions and contractions of her lungs.

Language wasn't needed to recall or create the memories. It was only a factor in communicating with people. "I had such a hard time getting the thoughts in my mind to translate properly. So, I eventually practiced talking through pen and paper."

Dear Flower Lady,

Weird colors zigzag in my eyes closed.

- age 4

5

Her pre-school teacher noted in a progress report from the early 70's, the little girl was a quiet child, but will talk of her life before this one. Something she'd remembered, "from before I showed up here." When asked about her states of quiet, stillness, or nature play the little girl described it as "nothing."

"I am not thinking of anything, and everything comes through me. It doesn't stay in my mind. It is like watching the birds or the flicker of flames and everything flows. I flow with it ...it doesn't attach to me. I am all of it and all of nothing at the same time."

Meditation has impressive effects on the brain. It has been shown to help increase memory by strengthening brain systems and the hippocampus. But, more importantly, it helps dissolve the division between one's self and the world. Where the passage of time is nonexistent by the assumed standards and knowledge expands indefinable by words. Like watercolor kissed by rain. Meditation blends the workings of all sectors of the mind and soul simultaneously.

As the little girl grew, nature's canvas painted places of fascination and worship with secret joys and knowledge. Intuitively, she became somewhat in sync with her father's feelings about organized religion. While her mother sort of pictured the family together every Sunday morning, sitting prettily in church, her father resisted the efforts.

"It's just superstition," he'd argue as scenes within his heart and soul clawed against the present life, crying for mercy.

~

A jungle closed, dark. Unmoving, men held their breath. Fear gripped the hairs on their necks. Pop! A shot rang out. All hell broke loose. An enemy tank trampled through the thickets before them.

"Fuck! Get down!"

He grabbed the shirt of a young boy in his platoon who had

begun reciting a desperate prayer.

"Our Father, who art in heaven, hallowed be Thy name..."

The missile launched; the boy evaporated. Only a scrap of fabric remained within her father's grasp.

~

Her mother though thoughtfully urged that no matter what he thought, it was "important" for the family to have a structure, a unity.

"But I don't have a belief," He said.

"Then you need to pretend you do, if only for the children."

Her father's belief in religion changed dramatically while he was in Vietnam. As a young officer, he watched the men in his platoon stand beside him, one moment full of life and the next instant, dead. While serving his tours, he kept a small black notebook with the names of the men in his platoon who were killed. When the tours ended, he traveled all over the country to meet each of their parents, sharing stories of their sons, hoping to help heal their pain. It didn't matter to him which religion each soldier had professed to believe in, for "God" played no favorites.

Just thinking of what he went through and all those who were hurt and killed. By abhorrent comparison, her father was lucky, wounded, but for all appearances, not maimed or crippled. His injuries, though, ran deeper than scar tissue; he suffered a delayed reaction that after several years drove him inevitably to repeatedly relive the ordeal on the Ferris Wheel in his mind. His dreams were filled with screams, with cries for help, and the horrors of fighting and killing with his own hands. His frustration with organized religion grew when he'd watched men praying desperately for their lives to be spared. He was not about to teach his children this false hope. He would let them find their own faith, through their own needs and experiences.

The little girl watched the changes in her father with a sort of curiosity, and started to make notes of the tiniest subtlest changes that would occur behind his eyes. The tiny pings of his uncertainty or fear translated into behaviors that created intense moments of unrest in his life and for those around him. He did all he could to hold onto any semblance of a "normal" life. He grabbed tightly to everything he thought he could control, and in doing so he began to tide with obsessive behaviors, developing domineering and manipulative personalities, and caught himself before violence took over.

It was on a night when one of her father's episodes was ruling the silence of the house that she tried not to fall off the roof of their home in Portland. Her teeth clenched a hold of her nightgown's hem, which served as a makeshift sling to hold the glass jar protecting a blue envelope. This allowed her to use both hands to climb down the tree just outside her parent's bedroom window. As soon as her toes felt the cool ground she took off through the night with the light of the harvest moon guiding her.

The woods of Tryon Creek Park were just a mile down the lane. She'd never ventured out alone after dark before, especially into the woods where shadows prowled helping the bandits and monsters mill about their lives. This letter was important, though, and needed to be mailed as soon as possible at the pine tree near the abandoned shack.

The rain started up again and the moss-covered stones next to the creek filled with water and offered no traction for hurried feet. She flew onto the ground catching herself before the creek did. But the falling and skinning her knees wasn't the worst sting, it was losing the jar. She couldn't see anything in the dark by the rocks because the amplified forest sounds hitting her ears were blinding her eyes. Twigs snapped, leaves broke, and the owl said something to encourage a quickening stride all the way back to the house, up the tree to leap across her room and place her warily back into bed.

Chapter 2

The Land of Ought Not

Once upon a time, tucked deep in the woods, there was a shack. And in addition to the fairies, trolls, bandits, and shadows that were never far away, a woman lived there. Her long hair moved as if autumn and winter danced. The curves on her body were soft, and her heart was like a daffodil against the grey spring sky.

On the far edge of this forest lived the little girl. And for her, it was a full-time job living alone amongst the busy lives of her family. The worlds in her mind were there long before she was brought into this one full of schedules that build boxes around the what ought to be, to keep out the ought not. But no matter how much she tried, the ought not was never far away. It climbed with the springtime ivy and sprouted through the tender flesh of autumn's ripe fruit. It scratched against the winter's sky with the nails of barren trees and drenched her shoulders with the glance of summer's sun.

She often went to the Land of Ought Not as she stowed away in closets, under her bed, or in the woods where she penned hundreds of poems, letters and theories and mailed them, buried in glass jars everywhere she went for thirteen years.

Dear Flower Lady,

It feels like life is a dream. And everyone has their own parts to the dream. But then everyone is in their own dream too at the same time I am in mine. And they are different dreams in the same place. I used to have a ghost in my room and there is another ghost in the room over the kitchen. I know he is there, I can feel him and there is like electric tickles on my neck and arms and in my heart when he is near. I told my mom about the ghosts. Then she told me about the people that died at our house. So, I think if they are still here and they tell me things and their memories. Then you are really real too.

- age 6

By the time she was seven, the world pulled her further into the Land of Ought Not where life felt harmonized and cycled. The outside world, the Land of Ought, stressed the importance of doing the things one is supposed to, of competition both passive and aggressive, and of focusing on goals so they could grow up and work in the same manner. A "You'll be happy when," kind of world.

Life was full of tests and tasks to complete, and it always seemed people went about life as if it were a problem to solve. For example, rather than letting the leaves decay beneath the tree to feed the soil, they were raked and moved.

"Who rakes the forest leaves?" She would ask every year.

"No one," was the simple reply.

"Then why do we have to rake our leaves? If the forest knows how be a forest, don't our trees know how to be trees?" She would ask as the combs continued their gatherings.

A task complete.

Dear Flower Lady,

There is a reason life isn't just a line from start to finish. I figured it out because my day isn't a straight line. It doesn't end when I go to bed. I sometimes wait to the middle of the night to feel the page turn into the next day. But it doesn't flip or swish or anything. I just keep going and then the birds start to sing and the clouds are moving and the sun comes up. I tried to feel if there was a giant's hand moving me like I was in his doll house game, but there were no fingers moving me.

My favorite life this morning was seeing the dew on the grass. The spider web near the fence. Everyone's life around here seems the same. Like school is a machine. I show up to learn the same as everyone else. But I cannot. Our questions have to be about what is being taught. That is the same at home. It's like an invisible fence on both sides of the road guiding us to the Land of Ought.

- age 7

It's been suggested that folklore is based on some sort of truth, but that we live in a world where the mind is gradually closing. Where tolerance is replaced with the ever-increasing belief in formalized doctrines and nihilism. One onset of these modern beliefs was marked by what is commonly known as the dark ages, where, unlike other periods in history, important records did not survive, leaving, in many ways, this era lost to history. Some say that to protect a fragile ecosystem of hallowed races a veil crept in over the lakes, blanketed the valleys, and then climbed the alpines to shield the mythical world from the brazen destruction of man. Sometimes, though, on rare occasions, the veil would thin enough for someone to reach through.

And, on the night the little girl tripped by the riverbank bringing the jar with the blue envelope to the pine tree, that is just what happened. A veiled creature named Untl, who looked like a cross between a wood elf and a troll, watched her dust her hands and knees while leaning against a fallen tree by the creek. His eyes moved to the jar that'd flown toward the low bubbling rapids, and he decided to breach the veil's barrier to snatch it.

He took it into the boulder tunnels that had become a place to house forgotten relics and secrecies. The tunnel floors were made from an ancient volcanic vent and lined in smooth onyx. Granite walls were adroitly chiseled into shelving by skilled fey artisans, and this is where Untl placed the jar.

"I tried to find the jar but it musta fallen into the abyss... or it might'a been stolen. I've got to get it back to the pine though," the little girl explained to her china doll, Kitty, as they hid the next afternoon in the linen closet. "the message was so important."

She laid back into a pile of laundry where her focus blurred overhead. Rain began to drip from the closet's ceiling as lightning rumbled over the distant hills of the Wild West where the Drifter started counting.

"One one-thousand, two one-thousand, three one-thousand..." He was counting to make sure the storm hadn't decided to change its course.

"'Cause I ain't changin' mine," he said.

The Drifter had finally made his way to the Northwestern territories from the Deep South. Skirmishes and battles scattered the entire trail. Most recently he was drafted to fight in the second phase of the Yakima War also known as the Spokane-Coeur d'Alene-Paloos War. He was tired of war and questioned the taking of lands from the native people. Now that he was released from Colonel Wright's command he had a chance for freedom, but with so much killing and screaming and bloodshed he wondered how anyone could find peace. That's all he wanted, no more pleadings clawing at his mind, and he set off to find a quieter life, thinking it'd be best to follow the Oregon Trail to the west side of Mt. Hood, "'Cause i'twas a'ready broken in."

Well, the trail might've been broken in, but it was not exactly like an old comfortable pair of boots as he quickly found out. The Cascade Mountains stood as sentries wielding ominous weather and provided accommodations for fierce predators. The mountain lions watched the Drifter curiously while he set traps to gather pelts for bartering. Grizzly bears and black bears raided his camp, eating the food he'd caught, and had no problem protecting their territory. He quickly learned the smell of a bear when it lumbered his way by the sweet pungent scent of death that coated its fur and rancid breath that dripped from the sag of its drooping lower lip.

After months of hunting, the drifter had finally gathered enough pelts for a good meal and a seat on a west-bound stage. Days passed in town trying to broker a deal at the trading post. Unfortunately, being new to collecting pelts, his offerings at the post were less than perfect and not quite enough for the trip westward. So, hoping to make up for his lack of experience in the fur trade, he tried his luck at the blackjack table, winning some and losing more.

Days went by and it seemed the longer he sat in town the louder the cries from the war in his mind became. He began drinking with hopes of drowning the images, and his nights were becoming full of sweats. His room was above the saloon where the whoops and hollers of the men and women below did nothing to help. Putting the bottle down he chose to set out on foot. At least when he was moving the bayonet of war lancing his soul was yoked into some control. The path was arduous and long. Stage after stage passed him by, with not even one stopping to offer the smallest drop of water.

"Well, that's gonna change," he announced openly. Then, as sure as the day turns into night, the Drifter became the Bandit.

It had been three days since he held up the afternoon stage. The horse he took from the robbery got loose the second night, and because of this, the Bandit was left on foot. Knowing people were looking for him, he took to the trees. The woods were different than those he was living in only a month before. Prehistoric-sized ferns followed the creek up river, woodpeckers foraged in the canopy above overgrown skunk cabbage, and squirrels jumping from limb to limb vied for a look at the newcomer. Beavers slapped the waters with their heavy, flat tails while building dams by the creek, and Douglas-fir trees whispered their secrets through the vast underground fungi pathways. The Bandit had just about found a place to rest in the understory when he stopped in his tracks. "Voices," his mind said warning his feet.

"That's whot ther' sayin', got the whole stage."

"No kiddin', how much was ther?"

"Whot, you thinkin' of jumpin' the Bandit?"

"An' why not?"

"Cause, ya dummy, the reward's more than whot was in that box."

The Bandit furrowed his brow and quickly tried to open the small box, but he didn't have the key. So, ever so quietly he started to dig where he was, between two lichen-covered boulders. The ground was soft. He got about two feet down when a rockslide suddenly shook the earth around him...and just as suddenly the ground opened up into what must've been an underground tunnel. The cave-in blocked both tunneling sides, though. Rocks lined the walls with shelves carved by artisan craftsmen. Beads, gems, and colorful vials adorned them. But the one thing that caught his attention the most was a simple glass jar protecting a blue envelope. Glancing about over his shoulders and with listening ears, he hesitantly grabbed the jar and took the note. And just as he did, a strange form of heat vapor rose from the shadows and moved in the margin of sight. The movement was like a gust without the wind. Branches swayed and the brook splashed, all as natural as can be, but eyes could be felt upon the Bandit's skin. He scrambled to climb out while a warmth of breath settled upon the nape of his neck.

He quickly brushed around his collar where his hair was standing on end. "Who's ther'?" No answer. "I knows yers ther', I a-aint doin' no harm." The air cooled with the cover of clouds as a drizzle started back up. "Jus' passin' through."

He clambered up the newly formed embankment using ivy as rope, pulling with all his might. Whatever it was, was closing in. He could feel it and he ran.

"Are ya kiddin' me?" the Bandit thought to the God above when the men looking for the reward saw him.

"Hey, hey you!" one of the men called out. "Hey, you ok mister?"

The Bandit groused under his breath and kept running.

"That's him! The Bandit!" The man tugged on his counterpart's sleeve.

Mud sloshed underfoot, causing the Bandit to skid over exposed rocks. He fell, and the men just about had him. That's when he threw the box from the stage to make his getaway.

He ran until he couldn't run anymore. Another day of slower running and rain passed before he found the old shack and bunkered in for the night. The next morning, he was starving and had to find something to eat, so he left.

Chapter 3

Fairytales and Magic Spells

When we are born we immediately start adapting to our environments. Our young brains are brilliantly lit with their electrical activity. As children, we are astounding inventors and problem solvers. The processes take place in a vivid form of an imaginary world where anything and everything can happen. Our minds play out situations in a form of virtual reality. It's kind of like when you go over a conversation and you come up with the response, "I should've said..." With children that thought process plays out constantly, where sometimes the "I should've said" shows up before the conversation and is tested out in the physical world. Like the tangible world, the mind's virtual reality is not always a peaceful place and the imagination is limitless.

The little girl watched as the family she once knew began to die. As most people do when an unexpected change occurs, she looked for a trigger to the change, a time or event that could be corrected to bring back the family she once knew. As she looked back she found the changes were already underway long before she showed up in this life.

"All the lives are connected, all the things that happened were setting up for now and that means the future is already set up too." So, she attached the most recent memorable shift as being the loss of the blue envelope. "Maybe if I find it..."

"I looked it up, Kitty," the little girl said, pointing to the definition she'd written down. "At my sister's school. She takes Latin."

"What'd it say?" Kitty asked.

"Origin." she answered.

"Origin? That's a person?" Kitty asked again.

"No, persona. That's the origin of person. That explains it."

Her older sister's tiara found its way off the shelf to sparkle as her crown.

"We are all hiding...and pretending to be something. The bandits are pretending. My dad is pretending. My mom, my sister, and even me."

Her sister opened the front door which hurried the tiara's return as feet slid over the bare oak floor and jumped to the soft carpeting of the hallway taking, her with them.

"You see," she continued, "we are all pretending because we don't know who or what we are."

"I don't get it. I just am," Kitty said.

"Yes, because you don't have to be anything because you already are, you already flow in the hum."

Kitty sat on the yellow canopy rungs watching her climb up.

"I mean, you are part of everything. You are love like the Brahma we read about in the National Geographic." The little girl explained. "But people pretend."

In the woods, she and Kitty pushed the rickety wood door of the shack open. Thick dust littered the floor, cobwebs scrawled across the ceiling, and a single shelf held dated books full of must and mold. Her fingers ran slowly over their bindings. Goosebumps flocked her arms as she pulled a book from its place.

"1926. That's how old this book is, Kitty." She read the binding, "My Antonia." She pulled another book down. "Here's one. Originally published in 1892, and this edition is dated 1919. The Diary of a Nobody."

She replaced the books to the shelves after wiping down the dust marks.

"This is the fireplace the Bandit warmed up by that night he stumbled upon it. He took his jacket off to let it dry out over the back of that chair."

She bent, looking under the chair. "No blue envelope," she said scanning the room for what seemed the millionth time.

She went to work dusting and sweeping the small space. "We can light a fire but first we need to check the chimney. That is what my dad says we have to do before we start having fires every year."

Soot fell like a blizzard from shoving a broom handle over and over again up the stone flue.

Looking like a scullery maid on a bad day, the little girl made her way home and snuck upstairs to the bath. Soon the porcelain tub looked more like a coal bin smudged in oily, sooty smears. "Woops."

It took several days' worth of work tidying up to get the little shack clean and livable, to remove all reminders of the Bandit. After a quick stop by the woodshed for tools, she was led by the giant ferns and banana slugs through the pines where the days awaited. She left and returned in clean clothes, thanks to Kitty's idea of storing work clothes in one of the pots at the shack.

"Kitty, if you think about it, we are all a nobody. We are all part of the hum. People shouldn't have to pretend to be important, because we already are. Just not the way we think we should be."

A fire lit, torching splinters and twigs. "We need a bigger fire to heat our pot."

Outside, dry moss caught on her sweater as she stacked small branches under her arms for fuel. Soon the fire warmed the small room and a cast iron bowl hung over the flame with twisted fence wire.

"We are going to release the walls of persona, Kitty."

Kitty's beautifully painted hazel eyes put their trust in her.

"We'll release spirits into the hum and be free. Let's be the witches of Macbeth; you and me, and...the Flower Lady will have to be the third."

Water from the stream began boiling in their makeshift cauldron and ingredients were laid out ready for inclusion.

~

Magic potion ingredients

Fiddlehead Fern leaves

Tiny bone found on the path

Freshly picked pinecone

Juniper berries

Elderberries

Moss

Mushrooms from the horse poop

Flower petals

Honey

Cracked open hazelnuts

- age, 8

The ingredients list was found buried outside the childhood home in Portland, Oregon.

"They're all substitutes, but they'll work."

A gathering of birds sang outside as the dusk held its breath for the spell's dawning.

"Let's begin. Round about the cauldron go."

They danced with the golden hue of firelight.

"In the poisoned entrails throw.

Toad, that under cold stone days and nights has thirty-one

Sweltered venom sleeping got,

Boil thou first in the charmed pot."

She looked over the displayed ingredients, "We'll just put in these rocks instead of a frog. I don't want to boil a frog, he's too cute."

The rocks splashed into the rolling bubbles releasing steam that twisted like an unhurried tornado, slow and mythological towards the ceiling.

"Double, double toil and trouble;

Fire burn, and cauldron bubble.

Fillet of a fenny snake, (the fiddlehead fern)

"In the cauldron, boil and bake."

Her eyes closed to feel the steam wrap her like a cocoon with a comforting embrace. It pulled against her back, branching like the tree, feathering like wings.

"Eye of newt and toe of frog," (in went the small bone and one juniper berry)

"Wool of bat and tongue of dog," (flower petals and moss)

"Adder's fork and blind-worm's sting," (mushrooms from the horse pile and elderberry)

"Lizard's leg and owlet's wing. (hazelnut and pinecone drenched in honey)

For a charm of powerful trouble,

Like a hell-broth, boil and bubble."

And she drank it while the steamed wings blackened like the raven lifting her into the kaleidoscope of the hum.

Dear Flower Lady,

It is hard to describe what I see without vision, when my eyes are closed. I've been looking through the dictionary, but it is full of words used to describe our limited view of the world. Limited because it's based on what our eyes can see when they are open. I see colors they do not teach on the color wheels. I see colors outside of the vision of my eyes. Everything is always moving and always still. It is filled with beautiful spirits and life is like magic. But not like magic tricks, but like fairies and science, space and atoms. A behind the eyes view of life. A world unspoken. Words are limiting.

-age, 8

Chapter 4

The Bandit Meets Untl and the Puppeteer

The Bandit saw smoke billowing from the chimney when he got back from getting food and slunk back into the shadows of the dense forest because someone else was already in the shack. The blue envelope weighted his breast pocket with a sort of novelty. Like one of the king's secrets! He took it out again and read the front, "Do not open until it is time." He stuffed it back into his pocket.

"Welp, migh's well git goin' an' find that sinkhole 'gain," he said to himself after he couldn't get back into the shack for another night.

"It was not yours from which you took, return the envelope to the brook," a raspy voice said surprising the Bandit.

"Who said tha'?" The Bandit looked around. "Stop yer foolin."

He wanted to run but was paralyzed in place like one of those frozen-in-place nightmares.

"I ain' got…"

He felt eyes tickling the delicate hairs on the back of his neck.

"Step out so's I can s-sees ya." The brush rustled in thicket of giant ferns. "I hears ya. Come out or–"

A pair of large ferny green ears stood like that of a dog listening curiously before the rest of his body emerged, "This is better, now that you see me?"

"Go back! I chang'd my mind! Get back!" The Bandit wasn't sure what Untl would do. "Don' step any closer or I'll—"

"You'll return what you took, to me." The elven-like creature stepped out from the ferns. Long fingers pointed at the Bandit from hands that barely peeked through the sleeves of his brown felt jacket.

The Bandit backed himself against a tree, "Don' come any closer. Please. Wha'ever you are!" His eyes squeezed shut, "I sware, I wa' jus' goin' t-ta return i'." He reached into his pocket. "I got it righ' here."

"Well?" Untl asked with his hand out for delivery.

"Naw, it's righ' here, jus' give me a sec." Trembling, he searched desperately for the envelope.

"You lost it!?" Untl's saucer-like eyes doubled in size.

"Wher' is it? I sware, it was righ' here in my pocke'."

"Where is it now?" Untl asked.

"The shack! Musta fellen out in the shack. I took a rest." The Bandit acted out his movements, "Jacket ov'r the chair. Lit the fire. Laid down to sleep. Musta fell ou'."

Half stumbling and crawling, the Bandit ran off. "I'll get it."

Candlelight flickered from the shack's windows against the dark sky like a painting you'd see at a museum where the smoke billows and the full moon sits above as if holding invisible strings to a marionette, which is the life below.

From the trees, you could almost see the puppeteer playing as the family sat to eat supper. The Bandit's mind had continued running without him. How was he to get inside to have the chance to look around?

"I'll jus' knock, an' maybe they'll feed me too." He nodded to

23

himself, "They ain' got no reason to be 'spicious."

He stood, pulling himself together, but not enough to ready him for the unexpected clammy touch of the shadow creature with breath licking at his earlobe.

"The blue envelope. You took it. I want it," the breath whispered. "I...want it..."

The Bandit looked, but saw nothing. "I don' got it."

Whatever the shadow was, its cold touch ran like a finger across the Bandit's throat, threatening.

"You will get it and give it to me."

"Wha's in it? Wha's in tha' envelope?"

The invisible breath chilled his bones. "Now," it said.

Panicked, the Bandit looked around. He just needed into the shack and, for the untold time in the last few days, he stumbled forward. The man inside refused to invite him for supper.

"Word's been spreading of a bandit, and I just can't risk my family tonight, mister. It's been a long day. Maybe in the mornin' you can join us for breakfast."

The Bandit slipped on the stairs going down, landing hard on the dirt. He couldn't go back into those woods without the envelope. That's when he saw the hatchet leaning against the fire logs. Dusting his knees off, the Bandit looked through the candlelit window where the family began acting strange, possessed even. To him it looked like the shadow creature might've taken over.

"That's it!" A surge of fear and fury raged within him – a venom so great it was unlike anything he had ever experienced before. The strings of the puppeteer moved him almost mechanically to the hatchet, up the stairs, and into the shack.

Chapter 5

Magic Mushrooms

"That's what bad guys do. They hide maps and stuff in secret places, usually under floorboards or in a book on the shelf. There were still books on the shelf, musty and old, so he might've put the envelope in one of them. The problem was a family moved in before he could get it back." The little girl contemplated her words.

"Why else would he have hidden in the trees while the family finished their dinner?" She asked rhetorically as her thoughts skidded forward to answer the next question. "It was a soup, a stew sort of thing. Probably rock soup. That makes the most sense; after all, they lived in the woods. And there are a lot of rocks."

"It would probably be better that the family didn't know they were getting hatcheted."

"But how would they not have known?"

Pacing with moss-stained white tights and black patent leather Mary Jane's, the little girl fashioned the story as her eight-year-old fingers twiddled in thought.

And that's when they caught her eye.

"Mushrooms! They ate the wrong kind of mushrooms in the soup!" Joyously the words escaped. "When the poison kicked in, they had no idea."

Kitty sat on the stoop with another questioning look.

"They accidently picked the wrong ones..." the little girl answered.

The doll kept looking at her.

"Because they were pretty, kinda purplish. That's why the kids picked 'em. And they put 'em in the soup – as a surprise!" The leap in her voice was convincing enough. "Now we need to find the envelope. Maybe he buried it in the lilac grove."

The little girl's mind stayed in the lilacs for a brief second before offering another idea.

"Let's make perfume," she said.

The small porcelain face sighed thankfully, ready for something else aside from the bad guys that seemed to always lurk in the shadows.

"We'll need to ask a scientist for help first."

From the top of her tights she pulled out a small note pad taken from her mother's desk and a pencil.

Dear Flower Lady,

Today we stopped the family from hurting. They ate mushrooms. They didn't know you to ask if they could eat them or not. Kittyflower and I want to make perfume. I think we need a scientist.

I miss you

- age, 8

Folding the letter as small as possible, she moved to the old pine tree with its root bent like a guard.

They bunkered indoors when they couldn't go out. A makeshift writing room sprawled with crayons, pencils, paper, and glass canning jars under her yellow canopy bed. The space, however, seemed to shrink the older she got, making it harder to reach the supplies or hide when she wanted to be invisible. So, the makeshift room gained satellite offices in closets, behind couches, under giant arborvitaes, in horse stables, but never in the basement.

"We can't go to the pine today, Kitty, so we are going to the rafters." Kitty hitched a ride in the back of her tights. "Need two hands to climb y'know."

The unfinished attic ran like a hollow garret with two levels. The first being the home of her father's desk at the far end, looking out a tiny window to the often-grey Portland sky, and the second, up a ladder to a labyrinth of boards without a proper floor.

She never dared to use the lights and went along strictly by crawling, feeling, and balancing.

"Don't worry, Kitty."

She weaved her way along as spiderwebs brushed eerie tales on her shoulders, and creaking boards whispered the future. Up the wall she climbed. Splinters bit her hands. But finally, in the highest eve, she could mail her letters.

"There, all done."

A chill set in around the quaint cottage (also referred to as the shack). It painted the spider's web with ice and kissed the grasses with frost before the late morning sun peeked out. After stoking the fire to warm to her tea, the Flower Lady emerged with a basket around her arm the way lovers stroll through the park. She greeted the edge of the woods where the deer were already snacking on blackberries.

"Good morning," the Flower Lady said. "Shall we check for mail?"

Daisy the squirrel scampered over to the pine tree's secret mailbox with harvest-filled cheeks.

"Ah. We have a letter." The Flower Lady's voice was like harmony, beautiful like the stony brook.

After reading, she refolded the parchment to place it back in the jar. "Everyone, I have news about the family."

The forest paused.

"They are no longer hurting. They have moved on and our cottage is rid of the bad guy. The posse caught him." The gathered creatures cheered. "It seems, however, the little girl needs a scientist. One that studies plants."

A blue jay followed her to the windowsill where the sun-tea was brewing.

"So today we are not making pies, but a loaf of bread."

Every day, always every day, she had tea and pies and cookies waiting for the rare passersby. Soon the scent of baking bread wiggled its way out of the wood stove. It glided through the meadow and slipped between the branches to the trail below.

Chapter 6

In Fairy-tales, Time Amalgamates

Almost 100 years ago a new field of physics was discovered: quantum mechanics. Physicists Max Born, Werner Heisenberg, and Erwin Schrödinger created objects of the quantum world. And according to quantum theory, these objects do not move along a single, well-defined path. Instantaneously they take different paths and end up at different places at the same time.

Right now, this theory pertains to the tiniest particles, which can also be present in a single event in innumerable ways. But I believe larger objects, much larger objects, which are made of these tiny particles can also branch off.

This is where parallel lives, universes, and dimensions happen. I like to explain it as a curious case of déjà vu. Imagine driving down the road and you approach and pass an exit, and instantly, for the tiniest second, a feeling washes over you as if an event had just taken place. Maybe a flash of vision or an eerie sense of feeling that you took the exit even though you're still on the main road.

Our mind is programed to follow only one of the trajectories, leaving us to believe we are on a seemingly singular path. The particles, which are part of us, that took the exit actually have the same belief that they are on a seemingly singular path, thus creating a "parallel" existence with a completely different trajectory.

Finding the letters buried by the little girl wasn't so much a parallel as it was a curious case where the past, present, and future of one of these paths converge.

Past: pre-letter or the writing of the letter

Future: post-letter

Present: the finding of both sides

Dear Flower Lady,

Only transiently does our spirit reside in a body while weaving a kind of French braid. Where time, events, and choices converge. And where bits of our spiritual matter entangle, again and again, before, after, and during our mortal experience.

- age, 9

It puckered. The air puckered and sparked around a set of stray granite boulders. Marmots stood for a second of curiosity before scurrying home at the site of his ungraceful entry. Brushing his knees and shoulders with the flip of his hands, he reached for a small transmitter from the pocket of his brown tweed jacket.

"Smashed," The Man said, looking at the crumpled mess of metal, not surprised at the luck he was having of late.

He was in the middle of what seemed to be nowhere, high in the mountains with granite cliffs caging the distance in all but one possible exit several miles away. He'd forgotten his lunchbox on the other side of the teleportation hold, and his stomach was offering up quite a protest as he bent to grab some of the sorrel at his feet to choke down.

Looking more like Jules Vern without the beard, The Man began hiking the descent while using a branch as a gentleman's cane. The marmots came back out, watching the stranger stop every few feet to write observations and notes in his small leather-bound booklet.

Usually his travels mirrored, in a way, the stories of H.G. Wells in terms of time travel. He was a scientist by trade and part of an expeditionary unit exploring the wrinkles in time and space. He had traveled so often that by the time he arrived at his present location he'd already been losing any sense of where or when he came from. He'd learned to live in the now, in the precise moment, and to absorb and blend patience in the undulating and unpredictable pace at which his life moved. It was through a wrecked stonewall that this unexpected gateway traversed. His last recollections before stepping through the vortex were of what looked like a hidden garden on the distant end of the sudden warren. And now without a means of proper communication he had to make the most of where he was if he were to survive. So, he set off to find his bearings. Several days took away the distance from where he started to the creek below and introduced him to a new travel companion, one that looked somewhat like an Irish wolfhound.

Weeks found The Man and The Dog exploring forests and mapping the expedition as their own cartographers. Food was limited, and the call for proper nourishment commanded The Dog's paths. Leaves crunched under his paws in the dry patches and squished between his toes in the mud until the bewitching scent of baking bread stopped his methodical tracks before he took off in a run.

"Dog!" The Man called. "Where are you going?"

The Man, being much slower, continued to pause every few feet just to look around. "Look, Dog, come back! Look at these plants." A pencil scratched over the parchment as his legs continued to do a blind version of a jog. "Hold on while I take some quick notes." His legs came to a halt after about two hundred yards. Whether his stops were made in sincerity of documentation or just from exhaustion, he eventually could only follow The Dog by guessing. When The Dog reached the edge of the forest, the breeze was gentle and the clouds tiptoed across the blue sky. Ivy framed a small cottage displaying warm bread in the windowsill beside the brewing sun-tea.

"What is it, Turcm?" the Flower Lady asked.

She stood at the far edge of the meadow when her raven left its perch to scope out the shaggy dog drooling beneath the display. Although, he quickly altered his flight plan to the higher branches as The Man appeared.

Dear Flower Lady,

I am glad the scientist came by.

He might want to try your blackberry jam. It is my favorite.

Chapter 7

When Things Just Get Worse

In the morning, blood slowly dripped between the floorboards like a metronome. Drip...drip...drip. The sky's grey coat slid into the evaporating mist leaving the sun exposed. Leaves scuttled about, finding their seats. The gnarled baton of the wise oak led the ravens' march before their song took off as part of the symphony in the Hall of the Mountain King.

There was no time to bag the bodies. So, the Bandit's only hope was down the winding path to the waterfall. There were lots of ferns.

He thought the man's body would give him the most trouble; it was large, muscular from labor, and stout, probably from the beer he consumed. The wife was easy. She just flopped over his shoulder. She hadn't bled too much, one hit from the hatchet and she was out.

It was the kids. They were the hard part. He doubled them up trying to save time, one like a sack of potatoes, and the other he dragged with her legs tucked under his arm. Her long braids, skinny arms, and hands caught on everything as they skipped across fallen branches.

"I ain' got time for this," he said unhooking a hand wedged

between two rocks.

By the time he got them all to the waterfall, the posse was closing in, and just as he rolled the bodies to the cliff's edge the world appeared to hold its breath.

"That'll be far 'nough, there, mister," the sheriff said, pulling the hammer back on his trusty rifle from behind the towering pines. "Let's get them hands up." The waterfall had done a good job masking their hooves with its insistent babbling to the brook below.

"Damn." The Bandit moved slowly from his leaning position over the woman's periwinkle dress. Sweat dribbled from his dirty brow, streaking a path like war paint.

"Watch it," the sheriff warned, seeing a blood-encrusted hand slip into the lining of the worn-out leather jacket.

The Bandit was quick, though!

His fingers were on the perfectly carved handle of his stolen Winchester faster than you could say "Bob's your uncle."

Pow!

A bullet whizzed by the deputy, barely missing his ear. Another shot hit the rocks on the far side of the canyon sending a ricochet down river.

"Stop now, mister." The sheriff's voice was cool and collected.

"You ain' takin' me 'live, if tha's wat yer thinkin," the Bandit called back from behind a fallen tree.

Soon there was a scene as if the revolution found the Wild West. Settlers from down creek armed their families and then set out on a manhunt. Sunset came and went. The horses were tied up next to the shack and the trackers moved in by foot. And it was too bad the pine needles were damp, because the Bandit ended up sending unintentional smoke signals while lighting his campfire.

"And that's how he was caught," the Flower Lady explained to The Man and his dog. "Would you like more bread?"

"You know, there's nothing I like more than homemade bread

and blackberry jam."

The Flower Lady winked.

"So, you see," she said, refilling the buttercup saucers with tea, "The little girl needs a scientist." Moving to sit, her hands folded in front of the roaring stone fireplace. "Someone who can help her in biology, and in making perfume and potions."

"Well, I may be able to help." The Man patted The Dog before settling into the seat opposite her by the hearth. "It's a good thing you were baking bread today."

Rain poured in buckets around the little cottage. It even leaked through the cedar shake roof in one spot where, naturally, the hanging plant was set to gather its drink. Smoke billowed from the chimney above, and soup simmered over the fire. The Man sat reading a clipping about a boy named Tom Sawyer.

"Looks like he found a map, but his is along the great Mississippi somewhere."

"Hmmm, all these bandits hiding maps. I received a letter today at the pine," the Flower Lady said in passing.

The Man put down the clipping, petting The Dog's head, "Any news?"

"Yes. The little girl got a chemistry set. She will be preparing an experiment as soon as the sun rises," she said while stirring the caldron over the fire. "Probably a potion."

"Good." The Man nodded in approval.

Telegram

Dear Flower Lady. STOP. I caught my hair on fire. STOP. Making a stink bomb. STOP

It stinks. STOP

- age, 9

"Creative chaos weaves intricate webs," came the words unexpectedly.

The Flower Lady heard his scratchy voice emerging from the forest. "Good morning, Untl," she said, acknowledging his approach.

"Hmmm. Good morning indeed. There was a newt caught bathing in the mud on the way over." His extra-long fingers plucked at some ivy.

"As he should be in the mud." She stood, tossing him a crisp apple. "Where's your adventure taking you today?"

"I don't adventure."

"Oh, that's right."

"But if you must know," Untl scrutinized the Flower Lady with his beady eyes, and his long ears flopped innocently to frame a mischievous smile, "I am looking for an envelope."

"It wouldn't be blue and have anything to do with a treasure, would it?"

"Might."

"You can look around. I haven't seen any envelopes, though." She scanned the meadow.

"I'll just...check...inside." He tossed the apple core up to her and distinguishably straightened his modest 3-foot stature.

Books stacked the dusty corners of the picturesque little cottage. Balancing scales, ancient scrolls, and the answers to many secrets piled in loose papers were stored in baskets. The Man and The Dog were sitting at the log table setting their plans for the day.

Untl unsurprisingly gravitated toward the silver scales and rough gemstones they'd found.

"I'm looking for a blue envelope," he said, turning an opalized pinecone in the light.

"Are you?" The Man answered. "The same one as last week?"

"Could be." Untl put the pinecone in his pocket.

"Haven't seen one, but rumor has it the Bandit deceitfully hid it after he found it."

"Possibly or not. Either way, wasn't his to hide." Untl looked at the papers, "Might be in these?"

"Might be," The Man answered.

Untl moved to leave, stopping only to replace the pinecone at the sound of The Man's clearing voice. "Fine. But know this, when the spider knits, the world entwines." He ran his fingers across the windowsill as if checking for dust. "See you later."

"See ya then."

Chapter 8

The Bandit's Fate

Like memory and parallels, another curious theory is that things or thoughts don't actually disappear when they are presumed lost. They simply go missing. Like a game of hide-and-seek when taking into account an idea in quantum mechanics that information cannot be either created or destroyed, they may alter or actually may become displaced.

Like the idea of a parallel life, the presumed lost may actually be just residing somewhere else. Hiding from the originating environment. Unlike parallel lives or universes, the lost can find its way back to the originating environment. It may return in different times or places with messages or reminders for the finder. It could be the things followed you into a branching of a parallel and returned as a form of correction – as if it were attached to a bungee cord stretched merely between the lands of Ought and Ought Not.

Sometimes though they never return.

The whole town gathered for his hanging. The overcast skies opened up to play a methodical hymn, in lieu of the absent drums.

Water cascaded over the brim of the sheriff's hat, spilling down his long trench coat. The hangman's noose swung in the wind without a weight holding it steady.

"You got anythin' ta say?" he asked the Bandit so closely that the rain parted between them.

"Nope." The Bandit stood defiantly.

"Not'ta word," their eyes met, "'bout that envelope?"

"Nope."

"Might save you from hangin'." The sheriff shook the rope. "Or might not."

The Bandit spit on the ground where it was lost in the rain.

"Suit y'rself." He placed the rope around the Bandit's neck.

For a moment, the Bandit looked up and fear crossed his brow. Shadows moved from tree to tree, closer and closer like a shimmering oil slick. Their words whispered in the wind, directly to his soul. "W-h-ere?"

Panic surged in his bosom. I don't know, his thought heaved as the slick-turned mirage leaping towards him, "It's–"

"Too late." The sheriff shook his head.

Dear Flower Lady,

There are two evergreens,

Tall amongst the rest,

outside my window.

I watch them almost every day.

In the wind they bow. Their branches on their tip form to look like beings.

Elongated face, razor teeth, sharp cheekbones,

39

crippled, evil hands, two feet taller, thinner than the other.

Rounded, defensive, returning upright with the pausing of strong winds, he hits back.

The wind picks up.

Razor Teeth bends toward the child.

He just holds his breath,

waiting.

My breath holds with him.

I can't let Razor Teeth know my fear.

Why does the wind always blow in his favor?

I watch all the time, out my window.

The child,

who I favored,

I think was threatened too much and one of his branches fell off.

He is turning into another beast.

They battle.

I don't like either one anymore.

But I can't stop watching them.

I will remember them the rest of my life.

I will not lose to the beast.   - age, 9

It wasn't until the townspeople went back to their homes and the Bandit was cut from the rope that they dared move from the trees where they watched him hang.

Untl climbed unskillfully down the evergreen. Being a mountain bridge elf, he wasn't accustomed to climbing trees. He'd grown up using fallen timber to make crossings over creeks and small rivers for animals to pass. Sometimes this was how his family hunted for meals, blocking the timber bridge to prevent the animal from passing. When it came time for Untl to set out on his own, he first worked as a grounds keeper for an alpine meadow. Eventually he became a keeper of artifacts through collecting and expeditions where he crisscrossed the globe preserving forgotten treasures.

"He didn't say." Frustration held Untl's words. "He. Didn't. Say."

An acorn flew upward, hitting his back with a giggle.

"You think he would say?" The tiny voice hummed more than spoke, zipping around like a dragonfly. "He knew he was wrong taking that envelope."

"Shouldn't you be hibernating?" Untl spat.

"We don't hibernate." A set of autumn dogwood wings flew past. "You know that, Silly Untl."

A few more fairies caught a lift on a rising air current as Untl defied it all the way to the ground.

He stormed off muttering, "Gotta find it. Gotta find that envelope."

"You're not the only one looking for it, Untl! You're not the only one!" the fairies' voices sang out.

~

"The Bandit should've told the family what happened and that he was afraid and needed help," the little girl said while writing a letter. "Maybe, if he had, the family wouldn't have died."

Untl crept in the shadows listening to her speak through the

41

window.

"Where'd the envelope go?" She wondered. "The letter was important. And now... it feels like... its gone forever."

That's what Untl was waiting for, a mention of the envelope.

"Maybe... it's..." She thought aloud.

"Where do you think it went?" he muttered from the bushes.

"I had it in the woods near the creek. I tripped and everything was lost. It was so long ago and it was like it just disappeared. It was the only blue envelope I had. And now it's just lost forever."

"Not forever," Untl thought, slinking back along through the woods to find the creek. "It will be found."

Turcm the raven scratched his midnight beak on the bark of the Montmorency cherry tree as he watched the little girl climb to mail a letter.

"Don't worry, we won't slip." she said between clenched teeth, carrying Kitty by the dress.

"Won't slip," the raven echoed.

A slight trepidation paused the climb.

"Turcm, is that you?"

"Won't slip."

A haze moved in, painting the bark around the little girl's hands just as they reached the small hollow between the branches. Her naked toes spread for traction.

"I've got you, Kitty. Don't worry."

As soon as the letter, wrapped in a sandwich bag, snuggled in for mailing they scampered home and the raven took the note with liberty, acting as a mailman.

"What is it, boy?" The Man asked when The Dog startled at the sight of jet-black feathers diving from the trees.

"Turcm, what's gotten into you?" The Man asked the circling

bird.

"Ltr."

"Huh?" The Man questioned.

"Ltr. Ltr." Turcm repeated. "mArrr-en"

"A letter?"

Turcm nodded, landing on The Dog.

"May I have it?"

Reaching into the down layers of his feathery coat, Turcm retrieved the tightly folded note.

"Thanks," The Man said, trading with Turcm for a piece of bread. "Let's see what it has to say."

He sat on the timeworn stone stairs outside the front door of the lovely weathered little cottage. The soft parchment of the letter ran between his fingers while he waited for the Flower Lady's return from the creek.

Dear Flower Lady,

Often it is the search for meaning that drives the actions of people. A reason or point of being.

People go about doing what they can to survive this life in one way or another. Sometimes they try to differentiate themselves to be seen as important. They strive for successes to elevate above their peers, and to try to prove to themselves they are not insignificant. This can be very lonely and then they have to pretend to be something they are not. It seems they push through life, barely resting for fear it will catch up and expose the truth.

But, everyone stops for a sunset. Around the world regardless of education or status. Why? Because the sunset is significant.

It is significant like the water flowing in the brook,

the silence of a still forest.

Or moss upon the weathered brick.

Significance is in the missed notes of a tune

or the crack of vibratos in the voice.

They offer significance by just being. They strike a chord deep within our souls because they just are.

They are what they are without the mask.

They just are.

They are the stars against the midnight sky,

the moon sharing an afternoon with the sun,

they are the gentle unplanned touch of a mother's hand.

They are not rushed or corrected.

We feel them with our souls because within us all,

at our very core,

we are significant.

To find the ability to let go of the race, to let go of the self, to let your spirit release into the hum, then the veil around us lifts and meaning begins.

Of course, our world is one in which we live by the beat of the modern drum, the clashing of coins in exchange for needs. I am not sure what is going to happen in the future. But, I wanted to say thank you. Thank you for listening. Thank you for being there. I know the envelope is somewhere. Maybe it wasn't exactly meant for the pine all along, but meant for something else. I am going to have a family one day and then I will be home. I will be the lady you were for me, and I'll bake pies for the welcomed passerby. This may be my last letter because my thoughts are empty of late. I'll never forget, though. I love you. Please give everyone a hug for me.

Eternally yours, Maren

- age, 17

Epilogue

Over thirty years passed as thickets grew and trees fell, filling in the small meadow around the rudimentary shack. The Flower Lady remained in Avalon while Untl and the fairies quietly continued their search for the blue envelope. Maren carried a gift of chocolate with her always. She ground the cocoa beans, she made special powders and cocoa pastes and wrapped small chunks of chocolate in parchment, securing them in twine for others to experience a small remanence of a fairytale.

The world within the world remained as a weathering book in her mind. Opening to share a few simple tales and gather stories in the years of her sons' lives. Here and there a giggle broke through, or a cricket sneezed and ivy draped from the binding, but eventually it sat upon memory's quiet shelf as the boys grew up and nightly phone calls replaced the goodnight wishes sent between the rooms. Even on this night. The night before.

"I love you, Mom."

"I love you too. Sweet dreams."

In the morning she got dressed and made her way to the hospital for a quick medical procedure. Her heart fluttered oddly like a pit fell in her stomach, a sense of urgency guided her thoughts to her sons, but she brushed it off as nerves.

The call came in leaving a message while she moved into the anesthetic and waited for her to come back.

With a groggy mind, she listened as the voice on the other end said, "This is the police chaplain. I need you to call me about your son."

Why would the chaplain be calling me? Did my son get married?

Her heart stopped waiting for her mind to catch up.

No.

Her hands shook as she dialed the return.

No.

With a shriek, she collapsed.

The breath. The breath of her son stopped upon a hillside and she was too late.

Months after the deafening call, when she was in the garden, the Flower Lady came.

"I miss my son," She cried, broken. "Please."

The Flower Lady brushed her hair gently and whispered, "He's still here."

Her eyes closed.

Rocks sat beside an aged creek bed beneath the giant ferns brandishing a secret.

"I know where it is," she sighed, "the blue envelope."

Beneath the brambles of holly and vine,

A jar contained a moment in time.

The clandestine night of devotion and fear,

Wrote upon paper marked with a tear.

A treasure was placed, a symbol of hope,

A fluttering heart retraces this scope.

Kneeling to dig,

Earth upon skin,

Reminiscent flashes pierce from within.

Cold upon touch,

It was felt in the ground,

A pause, a long breath,

This memory was found.

Dusting the dirt encrusted on glass,

Removing the lid weathered like brass.

There on the bottom,

Warmed by the light,

A simple blue parchment,

A folded note tight.

Written upon retrieval of the blue envelope in Tryon Creek Park, Portland, Oregon

Ever so carefully the intersection of past and present met.

Red crayon flowed with a beginner's cursive:

Do not open until it is time

The lip of the envelope shared the same penmanship:

Only you know if it is time

Within her mind the dusty book moved off the shelf. Memories rushed, reversing their pages. Twinkling eyes, and blanket forts, a baby in her arms, the runaway returned to a swish of the kite, and into the hum.

Sealed by antiqued glue, the envelope opened with a crackling release sharing the most important message of all.

Shadows held their position in the rustling breeze waiting for Maren to read. The fairies landed on the moss-covered rocks near the brook. Untl moved in closer. For all these years he'd not given up the quest and now the lost letter was shared. Maren sat on bent knees, a period of life coming full circle. Tears filled her eyes, rushing to the ferns with a blink.

Love is like the meadow's flowers,

sending seeds into the wind,

and it never forgets.

It never dies.

The weathered book dusted its jacket as the Flower Lady opened her arms, a pie on the sill as the sun peaked through the dark clouds, and everyone gathered around.

The book opened.

"Once Upon a Time..."

51

Where life has
no straight lines

53

The Buried Letters

The following entries are some of the letters found
buried in glass jars and other containers

The Journals 1976-1979

Today my dad and I flied kites on the beach.

Dear Fairies,

In case you are still here, thank you for playing with me yesterday. I don't have any cake, but I have this fruit loop that is kind of like cake for you.

Dear fairies and gnomes and even giants and trolls I believe in you.

Keep your heart like a secret garden.

Dear Flower Lady,

If there are cereal killers then why can't there be cereal livers. You know people who do nice things for others without getting caught? I will be a cereal liver.

There are fairies in the holly tree.

And something else nearby.

What is a new year?

    We left school in 1977 and came back after vacation and it is 1978.

    Something is telling me

    time isn't what we think it is.

Dear Flower Lady,

When I am in bed my body melts away. Sometimes I can make lightening sparks under the blankets when I lift them up fast. I wonder if those are real lightening sparks to another world much smaller. Is someone making lightening sparks for us? Of course, we wouldn't be able to see them just as they wouldn't be able to see us. We would think it is just nature and they would think it is sparks in their sheets, or maybe they are rubbing a balloon on the hair. Or rubbing their socks on the carpet and touching a doorknob. Maybe we are on a doorknob.

Dear Flower Lady,

What is the difference between lying and a theory?

Lying is saying something that is just plain incorrect.

Like did you cut holes in the sheets?

Then you say no when you really did.

That is lying.

Dear Flower Lady,

I never used to like the color pink. How the heck did I get a hair in my drink? Do other people shed too? Why do I always just see my own hair?

If I look into the sun, am I really going to go blind? I tried it and I was not able to see in a spot for a few minutes afterwards.

How about toads? Do you really get warts if you touch them?

What are the things we really need to know in life?

Why are lazy people and hardest working ones both miserable? They should both have time for laziness and hard work. Then they will enjoy things more.

What do people look like in Australia? How about in China? Do they really walk around in China hats that look like the seashells on the rocks?

You would think they would be foreign like aliens, but they look like regular people in the books, so what's the big deal?

It's not like we get to be Gulliver's Travels and really experience something new, something like tiny people or giants who have different understandings and ways they view the world.

I mean, when I travel that's the kind of stuff I would be interested in seeing. Like "Hey, we are going to Purpleton and wait until you see it! Everyone has purple hair and purple eyelashes and they make notes like a music box when they walk." Now that would be a vacation! I wonder what kind of candy they have?

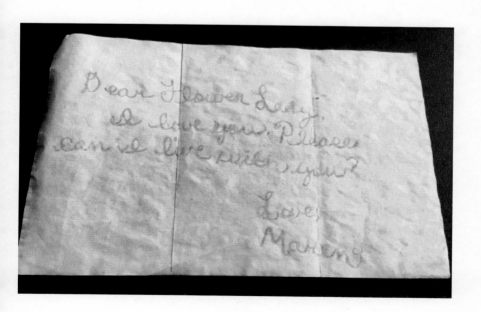

Dear Flower Lady,

Building the fort in the old tennis courts today we found a hollow beneath the pines. It was a natural hideout. We were hiding from bandits. Their footsteps crunched on the leaves, they were talking hushedly. They walked right over our hiding place. When they were far enough away we ran back to the pasture where the bright sun kept them in the shadows.

Dear Flower Lady,

The raspberries and blackberries are ripe so Julia and I climbed the fence at the neighbor's and had them for lunch but ducked when a car came and then climbed one of the cherry trees where no one could see us. It always feels like Peter Rabbit in the garden for a second but the berries are too good and just inviting us to taste them every time and there is always enough for all the other animals to not even know any are missing.

Dear Flower Lady,

   I know I can fly. I am just not very aerodynamic yet.

   From the dandelion, Me

Dear Flower Lady,

    I used to actually not like color because everyone was always asking me to pick my favorite. So, I picked yellow. But I like all colors, but I don't see them with my eyes, I feel them.

Dear Flower Lady,

I love you. Please, can I live with you?

Did you eat breakfast today?

Yes.

Maren, that's not breakfast.

But I ate.

I ate berries in the woods before lunch and it was after I woke up.

That is not breakfast.

Dear God,

Can you even hear me or not? Do you already know what I am going to say? We don't go to church. So, do you understand language? I can close my eyes and explore inside my body and it is a jumble of stuff. It's like a gaggle of tiny specks. Like a bunch of dots buzzing around. Anyway, what am I even doing here? Every time I talk with you, it's actually me talking to myself.

Dear Flower Lady,

What happens when the heart forgets love? The feeling of love? Can it know when love is there? Will the warmth return? Does the heart harden so tight it is gone forever?

Please don't let me harden.

Dear Flower Lady,

When I was little my dad shared a piece of chocolate with me. I wonder sometimes when I remember it like magic. I always chose chocolate when I get the chance to get a candy. And it's always to feel the magic again. It's like a secret that my dad doesn't even know why I pick the chocolate. But it's not the same when we buy it. It's not the same as when we just go buy it. The food of the gods is maybe because the gods are holding me when I hold the chocolate?

Dear Flower Lady,

The touch of sun came out today

And made the animals come out to play.

Before it left it touched the mountain

and painted a place for memory to stay.

In case you are lost, please return to the map that led you here in the first place,

and reverse directions.

Journals 1980 – 1984

Dear Flower Lady,

She was better than bad, but bad enough to be worse.

Her thoughts were selfish, but selfless in thought.

In her actions she moved with purpose, but the movement came without a sight.

Here is the quandary with life as lived.

For can she say she lived for life?

Dear Flower Lady,

Today I heard about old souls and new souls. An old soul is someone who is more peaceful and calm, and a new soul is someone who isn't.

I asked, "Can you be an old soul in the woods and a new soul in town?"

"No. An old soul is an old soul, they know how life works and they know the rules. A new soul is someone who has not been to life before."

I had to think about that for a bit. And this is what I came up with:

Follow.

If the old soul just knows how to be patient and knows the rules, they keep coming back to life. Then they must be ok with following what they are told.

We were at a stoplight and there was no one else in a car or on the sidewalks.

I asked, "Can we go?"

"No. We have to wait for the light to change."

"But there is no one else around, can't we just make the red light like a stop sign and go when it's clear?"

"No. The red light has different rules than a stop sign."

It's not that I don't agree with rules, but some rules don't make sense.

I understand the woods. There is harmony in the woods, even if it doesn't seem fair. But people are different. We make stoplights and aren't allowed to use our own brain to go when it is perfectly clear and safe.

It is like swim practice. I get in a pool and swim back and forth because someone told me to. Every day I swim back and forth because that is what I am supposed to do.

I am not an old soul, because I ask questions and do not just go along with what is told to me (at least in my mind).

Maybe what people think is the old soul is really the new soul like the ones that are not so calm. My little sister copies what people do because she doesn't know any better and it is how she survives to grow older. She is calm and follows the rules. It seems to be something of the same idea.

But the monk, the Buddha, they really are old souls. They know nature's hum.

Dear Flower Lady,

My dad took me to the cat show. It was like we were flying kites again.

We don't even have to talk because it was quiet love.

It was another day of sunshine near the Flower Lady's cottage. The Dog and The Man went for a walk to find some interesting plants to make a brand-new potion with.

But the rain came in and they had to pack up their greenery and head home.

The Flower Lady said, "Oh my goodness, you two are soaked to the bone. Come in and stand by the oven where your favorite treats are baking."

The Man and The Dog dripped all the way to the stove, and, of course, stashed their findings for later research.

I like it when she bakes the pies and drinks honey tea by the fire. Who does she miss by the fire? Why doesn't the missing go away? Is that why her heart is so soft? She held me tonight and I cried with her. I put the tears into Kittyflower. We fell asleep in peace.

Dearest Sunshine,

    Above the clouds you shine so bright,

    Leaving only a glimpse of light.

    When in bed I lay most still,

    Your warmth reminds me,

    My heart doth fill.

Dear Flower Lady,

   Sometimes when you think the coast is clear the eyes snap and then you want to run and hide, but you're frozen instead.

Dear Flower Lady,

This is a poem I wrote after our visit today.

To stroll across the country meadow, high atop the hill, the birds far flight it reaches, our hearts remain our still.

Beneath the tree, its canopy, hides the midday sun, to where I lay and count the leaves, leaving out not a single one.

Dear Flower Lady,

Independence and Belonging by Maren

Isolation can be on both sides of happiness and trapped. It can be gloom when you are unwanted in a group of people, it can be bliss when you are alone.

I am a plain creature. Therefore, my isolation is only enjoyable when I imagine myself free and alone with splendid thoughts of going home. I have no idea where that may be. Maybe I am only a spectator, an observer. Isolated with my own independence.

That is where my spirit hums.

Dear Flower Lady,

My dad was in a war. He has a bullet scar across his back. He must have been scared to be in a war. I asked him if he was scared and if it hurt and he said he saw a real tiger in the jungle. He said it was such a beautiful tiger that they watched in amazement and let it walk by their hiding place.

His sprit moved somewhere far away when he was thinking of the tiger.

I don't think I like war very much

Dear Flower Lady,

During lunch, I have been trying to read a book called Tom Sawyer. His inventor was a man called Mark Twain.

Why do I have to stay in at recess and practice making the middle part of the big M go all the way down to the line? Is the day going to stop because it doesn't? It is still an M. M M M. There. I just forget sometimes that is all.

I can't help that the words move all over the page when I am supposed to read out loud. I have to read to my dad and he is sad because I can barely read the book with one line about a giraffe out loud without having to make up what it says, because the words disappear.

I like the pictures though.

I sneak read my mom's Shakespeare plays and my dad's National Geographics, and the World Book Encyclopedias. No one would believe that I am able to understand them. Or that I even read.

Dear Flower Lady,

I come home as often as I can, at least every week. Or I go to the nurse's office when it is time to read out loud. I worry about reading out loud all day. Because no matter how much I practice, the words are always moving or disappearing. Because I can't read out loud, I am in the lowest level. But in my mind, it is different.

There is a special group of kids that go to a program in the afternoons sometimes, if they are really smart. I wish I could go. I wonder if they have a real science lab and make potions, and learn that time is only man made, and that I don't need to be able to tell time because it isn't real anyway! And that math is all rounding. Because one apple plus one apple does not equal two apples. Because the apples aren't exactly the same. I know this because I have apple trees in my yard.

Dear Flower Lady,

I don't know what the right things to say are, or what is funny or not funny. I always make mistakes. Always.

Dear Flower Lady,

In my dream, I was on the playground running with kids chasing me. All my clothes fell off and I was naked. But I jumped and could fly. And I was free.

Dear Flower Lady,

The Day the World Went Deaf

A daisy was unseen. It was stepped over. It wasn't seen passed the self, passed the center of adornment.

It died.

My sister has a book called Thesaurus. I thought it was about dinosaurs, but it is not. If you want to see more words for one word you can. That is where I learned about adornment today. It still sounds like a dinosaur book.

Dear Flower Lady,

Today I learned something in the meadow. I have this pen that can click multiple colors. All in one pen blue, and red, and green. It is an ugly looking pen. But it helps write in pretty colors. The woods can be scary, but The Man can find all the small things in the darkness that break it up and make it beautiful. He loves you because inside you are beautiful like my pen...

Dear Flower Lady,

   How many licks does it take to get to the tootsie roll center of a tootsie pop? It's better to just suck on it with lots of spit in your mouth and then crunch it when it gets thin enough. Be careful though because the outside candy is sharp and slices your tongue. Then it tastes like blood and grapes.

Dear Flower Lady,

My mom is beautiful and I love her smile. I love the salads she makes and I love it when she knits on the couch after dinner.

She has a blue robe with white flowers and also likes to needlepoint.

Here is where her heart is hidden,

   protected beyond the place forbidden,

   reaching to find his hand's own sorrow,

   without him now, there is no 'morrow.

   His fingers slipped from her own,

   his plea for help,

   it stood alone.

   The Flower Lady cried.

On my knees, I wept. Tears rolled from the depths of my soul.

Was it from sorrow or pain? Was it the marking of life, where sorrow renews with further understanding?

Where from ashes blooms life?

The perfect cycle.

Mostly unseen until time runs short and it shares the vibrancy of the petals and leaves. And even in their death their beauty matures.

May life's sorrows bloom.

Dear Flower Lady,

Thank you for the ladybug.

She was beautiful, against the grass.

She was very gentle, upon my skin.

She was very graceful, under the sun.

Dear Flower Lady,

It is the end of April showers and the first day of May flowers. It is my favorite day. One that leaves flowers in secret. I ring the doorbell and hide in the bushes.

Happy May Day!

Fireflies and ladybugs

and the stars kiss goodnight.

Dear Flower lady,

My mom left a note for me today I am mailing it with this note.

Dear Maren,

I love your poetry.

I love you,

Mom

Dear Flower Lady,

   The spirit knows the hurt and uses it for the canvas like the clover covered field.

Dear Flower Lady,

Date not to be determined.

I am writing this to show time's irrelevance to all material outside the human being. Only do humans count the minutes and seconds and years on the beginning of existence. All time is the same. I mean parallel. I mean we are here, right now. We are no longer then. We are only now. We are not yet there. We can only be now. That is why we are we. I am I. I will bury this and if someone finds it, they will probably be searching for time. They will get a surprise. Because we are in this moment together. Right now, because I am writing this right now, and they are reading this right now. We are in this moment right now together. Our moments are woven. In fact, it is probably starting to weave right now.

Dear Flower Lady,

Close your eyes.

The flower isn't alone. It is the whole plant, the roots and the earth, it is the meadow and the honeybees and bumble bees. It is the butterfly and the sparrow. It is the fog and rain. It is the sun and wind. It is your breath. It is mine.

Even in your mind. When your eyes are closed.

Flower.

Against the darkness of midnight behind your closed eyes it is connected and rooted. That isn't only darkness. It is the silence of the hum. The space between the stars. It is the cosmic between particles.

It is you.

It is I.

We are the flower.

The flower is I.

Dear Flower Lady,

This is an idea about where we are. I went to the office today to say I needed to see the nurse. I wanted a break from school. I sometimes just don't know where I belong except with you. But the neat thing I was thinking about on the nurse's bed pretending to sleep was if I ever wanted to go somewhere else I cannot. Because all of my somewhere else is where I am already. I can go to another place like to the library or the grass, but no matter where I go it is not somewhere else, I am there. Because we are already always somewhere else.

Dear Flower Lady,

    Maybe it was the first time I really watched her tend to the flowers. The tulips and daffodils. My mother was so careful with them. So peaceful. The pussy willow was in full bloom, the soft tufts lined the branches and I watched her.

    For the most of an hour, I remained hidden in the willow's branches, petting them.

    My mind was drifting elsewhere.

Dear Flower Lady,

I know my dad is good inside. I love him. He used to come to my school for lunch and he would try to help me read even though it was frustrating and disappointing to him.

I am sad he is sad and confused inside. I am sad he makes my mom cry sometimes. When he is not here my mom makes breakfast for dinner and she smiles a lot. She is very busy with all the kids and doing laundry. Sometimes when no one is looking she swims in the pool. I watch her through the upstairs bathroom window. I wonder how people become so graceful. When I swim I imagine I am graceful too, and that there is a sycamore tree and crab apple trees with tree frogs like at home. Sometimes I think my parents are going to get a divorce even though they don't ever yell at each other. But my dad has girlfriends and it hurts my mom's feelings.

I don't know

Yellow cake with chocolate frosting

and apples off the tree.

Just sit real quiet.

Be calm in your heart.

Move your spirit to the trees.

And you will find them.

Dear Flower Lady,

Today I was looking at the National Geographic magazine about cells. It was from September 1976. My dad has over a hundred National Geographics and I am careful not to bend the pages.

Did you know we have DNA? DNA is interesting. Do you think each piece of DNA probably has its own DNA? There is a part of the cell called mitochondria (number 10 on the cell map). It actually makes the energy for the cell to think and work. So, I think the mitochondria has its own DNA too. This is important, but no one can answer me and they just say nobody knows and don't worry about it.

When I let go of my brain and float into space it is like floating into a cell and into an atom. I think there is a pattern. Also, are we see-through if we are just a bunch of cells and atoms? Where does our spirit live? If we are see-through, then that means my spirit isn't trapped!

Dear Flower Lady,

Last week I thought about something amazing. Can you please ask The Man if DNA has DNA?

I also want to know why I always have the same thinking in my mind since I was really little? Are we born with thoughts already inside us? But why are my thoughts different inside, and I am a kid and having to learn how to read and do math and stuff outside?

Being born is like hatching from a chrysalis, and inside all the memories from the caterpillar are still there, and being a kid is like developing wings and we are learning because we have never had wings before, so it is fun, and hard, and scary, and frustrating, and confusing all at the same time.

I am going to mail this to you, but not at the pine because it is going to be dark soon.

Nothing beats lunch in a cherry tree.

Dear Flower Lady,

Last night my mind traveled into space. It kept going and going and going trying to find what is holding up space, because I want to figure it out. But this time I went so far out I was afraid I was getting stuck and wouldn't be able to come back. It was kind of scary.

Has that ever happened to you?

The Prism

A shatter, splendid.

Broken is beauty.

Break black,

Reverse the spectrum

Red, orange

Yellow

Green, blue

Purple.

My gift to you is broken.

Dear Flower Lady,

People are like toddlers in the scheme of life on earth. The plants are the wise. If we come back again after we die here, maybe we are learning more and more each time? I am not sure if we keep coming back though. But if we did, wouldn't we actually all be the same spirit then? So then if we treat others how we wish to be treated, then we are actually treating different stages of ourselves. So, if you want to be kind to yourself, be kind to all yourselves including the earth and plants and animals.

Dear Flower Lady,

   Today we are going to talk about cells. It is not so easy to find the information I am looking for. If the DNA is a map, maps can be altered. Does that mean DNA can be altered? I believe it can change behavior. I see it in the eyes, in the slightest twitch of a hand, faster than a second snap. It is almost like you can see the spirit look at the map and see two choices. The choice it was designed for and the other choice. When it chooses the other choice, that is when the eyes change really quickly. Like at dinner, and all of a sudden, your dad gets really mad and chases you upstairs.

Dear Flower Lady,

At the beginning of the summer we cleaned out the pool. It was all green and there were a bunch of leaves and frogs and water skippers. When my sister and I were scrubbing the shallow end, there was still water in the deep end. I went down to it to see if there was a frog. It was funny, it was almost like the water remembered me. Maybe it was my own memory, but later this summer and several times before, when we refilled the pool there was a kind of connection. At first it was new. Like meeting a new kid. But each time after it was as if the water and I knew each other. Like the water was happy when the ducks came to rest on the deck. It was happy when my feet dangled in. Its just a quick feeling between us before my thoughts go into the ripples when I swing my feet.

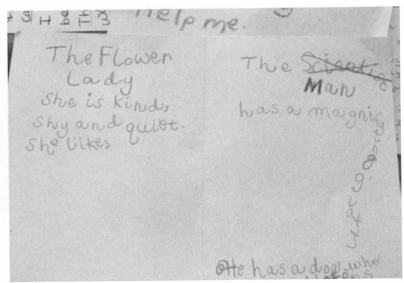

113

Dear Flower Lady,

It was a springtime cake. My favorite one of the year. Thank you for setting the table with daisies and hyacinth. I liked the blue jays whispering their songs by the table. The white frosting floated on the cake like the clouds high overhead. It was a white cake.

Then, I walked over to my old lady neighbor's house and she gave me tea in her garden. She was kind of like you but didn't have any cake.

I wish you were really here

Dear Flower Lady,

People eat plants and animals. Some people only eat plants because they don't want to eat the animals. Plants have feelings too. Life is a cruel game. A circle. In order to survive, we have to kill something else. We have to kill the tomato that contains the seeds to reproduce. We have to kill the carrot. We have to kill the bird. We have to kill the rabbit and the lamb. When we die, we will be feasted upon by both plants and animals. Plants eat meat. They eat the nutrients that feed the soil from the decay.

I think we need to make sure we remember to appreciate the foods we eat. That we do our best to not be cruel and to be thankful.

I am cruel sometimes with my words to my family. I don't mean to be mean. It just comes out. Mostly because I want to be left alone. And because I don't know how to act like them and I try and it comes out wrong and then I am embarrassed. If I didn't know my brother and sisters and met them at school, I don't think I would pick them to be friends with. I know for a fact they wouldn't pick me. They don't like me at all. They make me feel like what it feels like to go to swim practice. Sometimes I take that frustration out in words to push them away. I am not the same as them. I made my sister throw up one time because she said she doesn't like frogs. I didn't believe her and showed her the tree frog in my hand. She threw up.

My mother told me I am very lucky it was this

family who adopted me because otherwise I would have a different life. Maybe I would be in the woods reading a book like a nice witch. I would build a little cottage somehow. I would have a wood burning stove made from river rocks and make soups and have a garden and make pies and take them to the farmers market and feed the birds. I would have a bunch of books around and I would sit by the fire at night.

Love, Maren the witch of the woods

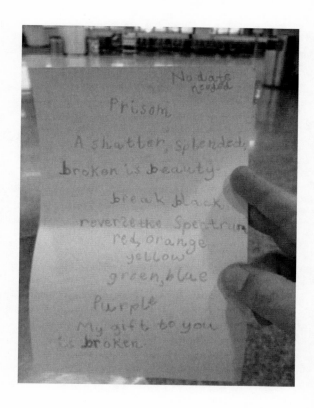

Dear Flower Lady,

This is what I found today. If you seek out kindness, you will find it. If you seek out anything, you will find it. You can always find the potholes because they are always there. Maybe the road repairman fixes one, but it just moves to a different spot. Always look for a little secret kindness even if it is really small and even if there are a lot of potholes.

Dear Flower Lady,

My best world is silence. There the conversation flows, the weather ripens majestically and life blooms with all the seasons.

Dear Flower Lady,

When I just let go, my spirit moves into the hum. In the sunlight beam on the carpet I can just lie there and become a dust floating in the ray.

Dear Flower Lady,

The Chrysalis.

Witnessing the outer change of the monarch chrysalis from emerald to reveal the inner monarch before hatching, she moved her thoughts into the unseen world behind the shell. A spectator can only understand what is in them, but she lived within the mysterious unknown, within deep secrets hidden behind the veil.

Helpless from the external world, the butterfly, the soul, absorbs it all.

Only when it emerges, the butterfly shares its beauty and peace. But when attacked by a predator it no longer worries. It already knows the poisons of the world. In the end, no matter the cause, the monarch leaves silently, marking only its colors as part of nature's magnificent evening silhouettes of hope, love, and comfort.

Dear Flower Lady,

The word on my sister's calendar today is "immaterial."

Within the Closet

Life became unbound,

No need for anything.

Simple pleasures, heart content,

the joy of writing merriment.

Without a name, without having to be what others expect you to be, you can become immaterial. When you become immaterial you never feel lonely. You blend into harmony. And you are free.

Turcm is me, Maren

Dear Flower Lady,

   Sometimes I think I try to fill in time with chores, or planting flowers for you, cutting Barbie's hair, or collecting 100 caterpillars, and sneaking into hidden places. Then maybe I forget to stop and feel the air on my skin. Maybe I forget to hear the birds talk to each other. Maybe I forget when I am walking on the grass that it is alive. I don't want to forget. Please help me to remember always to listen and feel and remember.

There is something to be said about savoring. Imagine if we learned to take the time to savor our food. To savor the sunset.

To savor a hug.

Imagine if our actions moved in time with savoring. If we savored the preparation of a pie. To savor the interaction with others. Our slowly built passions would burst with flavor.

Our hearts would be lighter.

Our laughter more pure.

Our pain better understood.

Dear Flower Lady,

They are changing. The emerald green was dulling and is darkening to black and orange. Except one. It must've had a fly on it. Maybe it is just a slow developer.

National Geographic has a picture in the magazine with millions of monarchs on a tree. There is a town called Pacific Grove in California where all the monarchs stop before they go to Mexico.

The article says lots of tourists go every year to see them. I want to go, but want to be alone with them. Where is Pacific Grove? My dad says it's near the Redwoods. How do the butterflies know how to get there? It would be great if my room was filled with trees and butterflies flying around.

Dear Flower Lady,

Humans need emotional intimacy.

Imagination is mine.

Dear Flower Lady,

I hate school. I am in 4th grade. I really like my teacher though.

Today a girl passed around a piece of paper that said, "Do you like Maren yes or no?" Then the whole class marked if they did or didn't. When it passed by my seat I didn't mark anything. I just passed it along. Then at the next recess I was invited to play on the field, and when I got there the kids circled around me and I got in a fight. I thought I would be able to win, but the first punch got me in the eye and it hurt and I just fell to the ground and let them win.

Then my dad picked me up. Then we went to the pool and I met Greg Louganis and Wendy Wyland. I think Wendy Wyland is really pretty and nice. She was the platform Diver of the Year this year. Someday she might be in the Olympics. I still like Nadia Comaneci and have a music box of her on the balance beam my Grammy gave me. I play it all the time.

Dear Flower Lady,

If life is nothing more than a string of elements, a pattern of cells, of imprinted DNA, then what is the use of living? What is the use of letting feelings feel? If all we are supposed to do is make babies to make more babies, then why do we love? Why wouldn't we just make sure the babies survive, and form no attachment, and then be done. But that is not what we do, and it is not who we are. In fact, if you look inside other animals, there is a lot more than just animal instinct.

If you take the time you can actually make friends with a tree. And the tree will truly know you. This is for all plants too. Plants really can communicate.

Dear Flower Lady,

I am going to be so happy to have kids. They will be boys because I want to build forts, and have big fires, and find fairies, and ride bikes, and I want to live with them like Peter Pan and Tom Sawyer.

Dear Flower Lady,

　　The moonless night is brilliant with stars. Please let me slip into their mysteries, let me dance within the fairytale of eternity.

Dear Flower Lady,

Our fairies aren't the same ones exactly that are in England and Ireland because they have different places to live, even though they are similar. In the Childcraft books you can see pictures of other places where people live. In Ireland and ngland, they have a lot of rain and hills and mountains.

Flower and tree fairies change depending on the time of year. It is like a fairy is the same depending on the type of flower or tree, but it is changed ever so slightly depending on their environment.

Kind of like if my real mom decided to keep me, I would be the same girl, but different because where I lived would be different and the things around me would be familiar, but if I were to see them right now they would seem odd, and I would want to come home to my mom here.

But maybe. Maybe, maybe is too far away and I should come home to here now.

Dear Flower Lady,

It's a rare occasion to the holly tree.

I wish I'd go much more.

Not only are the fairies there,

but hidden, a secret door.

The birds fly by watching me,

Curious to why I'm there,

The leaves are sharp and deeply green,

Don't touch them unaware.

A ring of toadstools vividly red remains a circle you mustn't tread.

But within the branches,

Protecting like a knight,

It's there it lives,

Magic's insight.

Dear Flower Lady,

I asked my mom if she changed when she became an adult. If she transformed and left herself as a kid behind. If she could remember what it felt like and what her thoughts were.

Because I feel the same, all the time. I felt the same when I was two and three and four. I felt the same when I was a baby.

She said people don't remember being a baby. But I do. I do. I remember it. I didn't have words then, I still don't unless I am writing. I remember something else. Something I can't explain and it confuses me or makes feel trapped because you can't go backwards and get what you're looking for.

She said she is the same. That she is the same girl just in an older body. That made sense to me. I am glad she told me that.

Dear Flower Lady,

My dream last night was about when I first started here.

There was a great light, so bright it wasn't even white. It was hot like a flash, and then I was warm like the summer sun and it was dark. Then it was like when your ears listening to your breath and your heart beating, but it wasn't my own breath or my own heart.

Dear Flower Lady,

Why I tap my forehead.

Why I tap my heart.

When I tap my forehead, or press a finger upon it, it opens up my thoughts outside the bounds of bone. It shows me calming libraries in the universe.

When I worry or need to calm myself from sounds around me, I can tap my forehead.

My heart is tapped to remember love, and to be irrelevantly me.

I tap because it is calm.

Dear Flower Lady,

It was at night. I could hear his steps on the wooden slats. The room was dusty near the end of a hallway. The handle to the door began turning and I jumped out of bed looking for a place to hide. I picked behind the door. There was no other place in such a short time. The door opened hiding me behind it. Then he said calmly, "I know exactly where you are." ...

He moved the door to look behind it. I felt my death. And now I am here.

I remember that life.

I also remember another one.

I was in the woods. But its not where I was born. I was born in town and moved to live beside the brook. You came from this life. I'll never forget you. It was before cars. We went to the miller's farm for our wheat sometimes until they were afraid they would get into trouble for knowing us. In the cottage by the brook it wasn't in America. I was always in bare feet when I could be. There was a man. He would visit. He came to the cottage through the woods. He was a part of a secret society.

I know he believed in the more. He believed in the secrets of the earth, the universe, and the veil. He was part of a secret protectorship. When you died I could still feel you. I know I got old, I lived alone in the little cottage and helped people who came to me. Just like you did.

When you died I was by the brook. Men on horses came searching for you. It was a sunny day, you could tell because of the light peaking through the trees. I can still feel the cool rocks and the sound of the horses being tied up on the other bank. They walked through the brook. It was a group of men looking for the men that protected the secrets. They didn't see me, or they ignored me. I was young. I remember when they took you. I remember when our eyes met. There was an understanding, a goodbye that wasn't a forever goodbye. But I never saw you again.

I didn't talk for a long time. Not even to the animals, I just sat. I sat in the on the steps. I sat near the brook. And at night I sat near the fire. I didn't ever really talk much again unless there was something to say. I was mostly silent. The animals were my friends until I died when I was quite aged.

I can still feel your spirit with me.

Dear Flower Lady,

Sometimes all that was needed was a bit of fresh air to calm the feeling of waiting.

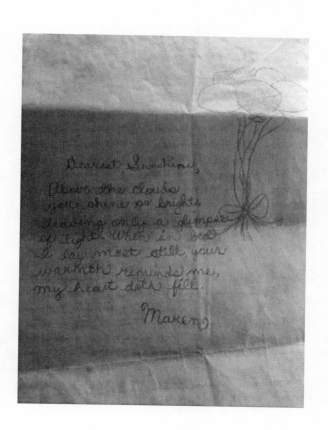

Dear Flower Lady,

Today the sun broke through the clouds and it glowed like an apricot against the sky. I will remember to share this afternoon with you someday when we meet.

I will give you apricots or make you a basket of fresh fruit and cookies. Do you like dried dates in December? They are like candy.

Dear Flower Lady,

As I lay in the yard in the summertime it can feel like I picked up right where I was before. That I am the same me.

I am connected to me. I am connected to the me yesterday and all the yesterdays and I am connected to me tomorrow and all the tomorrows. I am connected to them all right now. I am connected to all the tiny, tiny moments. And I can remember.

I can remember happiness in the darkest and most beautiful bright white light that was all the colors and music and everything.

I remember colliding to create the me that moves here. It was soft and warm, it thumped with a heart and jiggled with a smile. I remember the hum that purred with the breath.

I remember because I am still there. Pieces of me remain and are connected like breadcrumbs on the trail. Breadcrumbs that are already laid before the present me. Laid before my toes and behind my heels. Connecting it all together now. There is no tomorrow without yesterday, there is no yesterday without tomorrow. And so, as I am, I am not here.

Dear Flower Lady,

October mists are my favorite. The colors behind them play.

The songs and chatter from the woods greet the foraging day.

In the evening, the fire sparks and cider steeps above, where hazelnuts crack and chestnuts roast, and moon floats like a dove.

Dear Flower Lady,

It's the raven that calls my name, that shifts my spirit to fly, that teaches me its songs.

It's the raven I call Turcm who shares its eyes for me to see.

Dear Flower Lady,

We are doing dividing again in school. Well, an introduction to fractions and decimals. When I think of multiplying and dividing I think about jumping forward and skipping backward. Where plus and minus are walking forward and backward.

But fractions make no sense the way we have them set up. I asked my teacher why there so many left overs. Because that just makes math more of estimation than it does an exact.

Why should 1/3, when changed to a decimal, have a forever number of 3s after the decimal, but when we are learning to tell time and 1/3 of a clock is a clean 20.

Maybe the math we are doing is hard is because we aren't using the circle.

And if we make the circle like an orb then the math would be even more clean.

But probably I am just finding a way to get out of doing my work thinking about this. That's all for today.

P.S. I miss you

Dear Flower Lady,

    Lava spewed in the east as a voice reminded them of the haunting beast. Death's long hand, it finds us all. So, enjoy your life before you fall.

Dear Flower Lady,

The grass and ground absorb me. It is where I blend right in. I spread to the trees, I dine with bees and catch the wind before me. From there the current catches me, to the clouds and space above, to where the universe opens and the feeling is only love.

Floating

Dear Flower Lady,

The note on thoughts of the DNA's DNA.

Don't you like my pen? The tip is tiny so I can write neater. Today I laid in the clover, the bees buzzed around and tiny moths skipped all around beside me. I looked at their tiny wings and the petals of the clovers and I also picked a bunch of clover, after the bees got their honey, to suck on them. I love that flavor and the secret that is hidden in plain sight. That is what made me think of the Nova show my dad was watching on DNA. DNA is a string of cells that make us who we are. They are tiny, but scientists are exploring them. But there is something more powerful than that DNA, it's the DNA inside further. The structure of it makes sense. Like the universes that are made up of a fabric. The cell has a power plant that feeds it. So, it would be the mitochondria's recipe. So, if this is the case, then maybe it's not just the recipe for physical characteristics that the Nova program spoke about once, that we could program what we want our kids to look like, but maybe it is kind of like a food, of sorts, for the cells and are what cause cancer or transfers things like cancer, which is the disease that is talked about in 'Brian's Song.' I wonder why he sat in such hot water to feel better. When I was imagining the cancer cells last night, I think that is where the transfer is that spreads it. In the silk fibers of the moths, that is the food to the larger DNA.

My Hand

Holder of the future

Full of hopes and dreams

Scarred with defeat

Decorated with success

Warm and soft, it holds my life

Dear Flower Lady,

When you lay in bed, plug your ears and hum. Hum and feel the waves. They spread everywhere and nowhere. Take long big breaths so you can hum for a long breath. You can hum high and you can hum low. You can find the hum that makes you disappear like a warm hug's glow.

Dear Flower Lady,

    The sun set against the misted sky.

    Shattering the light before my eye.

    To witness silence, the beauty break,

    It is almost all one can take.

    Directed to the connection's own

    We stand in awe

    We're not alone.

    Maren

Dear Flower Lady,

Today we are talking about control.

From my observations with those around me, I find control or a lack of control to be quite limiting and offers a direct affect to those around them.

Rituals and patterns. Typically, you can find creatures of habit or those who lack control. Because when they have the same schedules and the same routines it helps create a sense of control.

Ultimately in our lives we have no control over what happens to us, and we all end up in the same place in the end no matter what we have achieved or accomplished.

When a person becomes more rigid, they become more dominating and control more and more. When they cling to this control, their lives actually become more chaotic as they keep grabbing at things outside their own.

This shows them over and over they have no control, and they become angry in their words or physical actions. They never settle down, they also revert to patterning, focusing on goals and mile markers. When they don't get their way, their actions can seem patient, but the loss of control steams inside until they snap.

The closet is my escape away from the control outbursts. It comes to a point that no matter how much an apology someone gives, it no longer counts because words are just air.

Gaining control, true control, is to know there is nothing to control. There is nothing to grasp. So, you don't have to let go of anything because you are already here, inside the hum. Just let it drape and drip over your heart and soul.

There is a difference in love. A calm union.

One like the flowers and the autumn leaves.

The winter's hibernation where hope and tenderness prepare for life's harsh cycle once more.

Love isn't a flash,

It's a mysterious depth.

Dear Flower Lady,

Cancer has been on my mind. I don't really know what it is exactly, but when I read the book 'Brian's Song' it gave me a name to what I saw.

My sister likes backrubs. She is almost 6 years older than me and pays me a quarter to give backrubs. I like it because it is quiet and peaceful. She lets me listen to John Denver in her room sometimes too, or look at her little dolls.

A few weeks ago, I was giving her a backrub by the fire in the family room when my dad was watching 'Sunday Morning with Charles Kuralt.' It was different though. When I give her a backrub, I like to imagine the energy of blood flowing into my hands like a magnet, and when they move, her muscles and blood follow and move like a warm soft ocean of clouds. But this day was different. She felt different. There was a tricky area that wasn't the same, it had a slightly different energy. It was a cell persona. So, I kept returning to the spot and she got frustrated with me a little, "Maren, finish the backrub." So, I did, but not very happily because my mind was stuck trying to figure out what was wrong. And it wasn't a tight muscle, it was a different energy.

Then it came to me a few days ago. She has cancer. She was in the shower when I told her and she told me she was never going to talk to me again for saying something like that. I told her because I don't want her to die. I would rather have it so she doesn't.

She doesn't believe me and neither does my mom, that she has it. But I told them it's only in the recipe part of the cells and it hasn't fed the them yet. They think I am crazier than they thought I already was.

I hope I am wrong.

Dear Flower Lady,

Without eyes to find ourselves, we would just be. We would just be. We would be natural and blend into the hum. We would just be.

But it is hard not to go look at what others see when they say things. I like my life without the mirror better. I like just being. It is too hard to be what is supposed to be in the mirror.

Love, Maren

Dear Flower Lady,

I overheard one of the popular girls talk about her new pair of blue jeans. They all seemed so taken in by them. I got the nerve to walk up to her and ask what kind of pants she had and she looked at me and said, "Duh. Guess."

How am I supposed to know what kind they are if I have to guess?

Then last week I was at the shopping mall with my mom to get a birthday gift and walked by a store that had "Guess" blue jeans. I felt silly.

That's all for today,

Maren

A pencil without an eraser still writes.

To exercise obsessively in the pool or gym is dangerous. It is disconnecting from nature.

Be outside, run with naked feet and the breath of the trees. Be with the earth and drink the bird's song.

Dear Flower Lady,

I thought of an observation. It seems to me that to always look at the positive side of things is almost as bad as looking at the negative side of things. The "things," whatever they are, are not solid though. They are not two-sided. The hold on always being sunny or an Oscar the grouch serves no purpose for anything good. It is destructive to the person themselves and to those around them. It is important to allow the thoughts and feeling move through you. Your body is not solid at the molecular state and doesn't hold on to these things. It is our ego that does. Always looking for the bright side or the negative side discounts the whole. It minimizes your feelings and those feelings around you, so the feeling of wholeness within the hum is pushed aside.

What do you think?

Dear Flower Lady,

No one ever promised you a rose garden. That's what a saying on my dad's wall says. When I was little, we flew kites. The weather would turn and the rains would come in. The ocean was unpredictable and dangerous one day and calm the next. But we flew kites and looked up into the mist.

What is love? Is it making people do things they don't want to do because it'll put hair on your chest? I never told anyone this, but I don't like water. I have learned since I was young to get into the water and ignore the feelings. But I love the rain. I love the rain and the brook. The water is happy. Watching the ocean, the water is happy, even when it is rough and wild. But a swimming pool isn't. The water in the sink and bathtub isn't free.

Is water alive? When it is trapped in the pool, does it get depressed? Like Shamu? It's like going to swim practice. The water, who is filled with chlorine and burns your eyes, who is sad because it is stuck in the pool. Shamu is stuck swimming in a tiny circle. Shamu doesn't even get the chance to play in the ocean and stretch out like the bird's flight.

I think water is happier in the brook. It talks to the energy of the forest, and the desert. The water that is bogged, that has thick sickness growing in it is dying too. It is decaying and being eaten with bacteria. It is part of the cycle of life.

Does loving Shamu mean keeping him in a tank and not flying kites, feeding him fish when he does what you want. Does Shamu feel loved? Does Shamu think that's what love is? That love is going to swim practice, and swimming painfully back and forth for hours for no real point. It is not like working on a family garden where you get tired and dirty and sweaty, where you tend the plants and share the appreciation with the earth and the family for working together.

Without swimming, you are not loved. That's what it feels like. So, when you love someone or something you push them to do things that after years becomes torturous?

I know there are a lot of kids who like swimming. I like watching them be able to just jump in the pool and talking with their friends. I always wonder how they do it. It is so curious for me to watch them. I try to learn how they can do it. I tried asking my older sister how she does it, and she just said, "It's not a big deal, just get in the water." I hug the wall behind the blocks hoping to blend into it. But my parents are there and watch me. They love me. They want the best for me. My dad signals for me to get in and I nod and cry in my goggles so no one sees me.

Is this what love is?

I can learn discipline and resilience by learning and exploring the world around us.

That's all for today.

I love you like the trees love the earth and the birds love the song.

Dear Flower Lady,

Sometimes I wonder if there is something wrong with me. Often myself slips into an opening somewhere in the realm of my mind. The opening is always moving to different locations or under different circumstances. From what I have observed over the years, there are several different degrees to the openings. I can feel the shift as if it were a change in elevations, not that my ears pop, but it's something like the pressure that signals you're elsewhere.

In several of these stages I am able to look upon my body as if I were outside it, this includes my thoughts and memories.

If someone were to look inside, they may classify me as having multiple personalities, but I do not. I am in meditation. My spirit is the same spirit just visiting altered states. Like I am the same me in the Grand Canyon and I am the same me at the beach or in the mountains. I may act a bit differently in those locations depending on the weather or if I am nervous of the water or fearful of heights, but I am still me.

As I write this I am currently in such a phase or state in my mind. Entering this first phase is letting the world pass through you. Like poking thousands of small holes in a plugged water hose and gently allowing the water to release its pressure as it drips back into the earth.

For me, the first time this phase was given a sort of recognition was when we watched a movie in school where a baby monkey had two metal moms in a stark room. One mom has fur and was warm. The other mom had an exposed metal body but it had the nipple to drink its milk.

It dawned on me I was acting in a similar fashion when entering meditation at a very young age. My meditation was the warmth and comfort and my life was the nipple.

It is interesting to connect this with the first level of meditation. Love.

To enter it is allowing love and compassion to consume me as a whole as if it is protecting the piece of spirit that is tethered to my mind. It is removing words to describe the views passing through your eyes and the sensations over your skin. It is letting them be as they are with no labels.

Love and compassion are almost like an entity of their own, but still a part of you. It is like entering your bed, soft and warm, with a blanket as heavy as yourself was pressing upon you like a hug. Once this sensation begins, my body seems almost numb. Almost as if it is disappearing into the air. But it is not actually numb because I've learned to go about my daily activities like school and swimming or pouring drinks for dinner while slipping into this feeling.

Of course, when this feeling first began, it was only when I was in my bed or laying in the ray of sun through the window. It felt so wonderful that even at age 3 or 4 I'd wait patiently all day to try and find it when I'd lay in the sun or beside the fire. I enjoyed the feeling so much I began practicing recreating it on my own, and learned to keep it with me.

This was the first step into a living meditation. It wasn't anything extravagant or counting stairs or soft music with a melodic voice guiding me. It was something very simple and natural. It is a state of being that is the depth of all other feelings.

Then one day I got into bed and began over thinking. "What was the first word?" "Who chose an apple to be an apple?" "How far can my mind go into space?" All three questions began a sort of trance. A meaningless chant. "Apple. Apple. Apple. Apple. Apple. Apple. Apple. Apple. Apple. Apple. Apple. Apple. Apple. Apple. Apple. Apple. Apple. Apple." And so on. The sound vibration began to ebb and flow like the tide pulling in the sunset, darkening into black, sinking into the abyss of space, dotting with stars, and venturing out, out, out, into the farthest space, farther and farther, my spirit and the increasing edges of the universe converged. I was space, space was me. My heart slowed to almost stop, it was almost to the point of no return. I was getting stuck outside this body. I had to come back. I forced my hand to move. To feel the covers, and I returned.

I knew my physical body didn't go anywhere, but I also knew I had. But how was that possible?

It was a few months before I tried it again. I was almost afraid of it. Almost afraid I wouldn't make it back. But I went. This time moving my thoughts slower. I'd stared into my eyes to find the surface of the moon. If you lean into the mirror and really look into your eyes for a while strange things happen. The rest of the room melts away and so does your face. They kind of pulse from big to blurry to small and tight to blurry all while your eyes stare back at you.

I can change the interior of my eyes by changing my central emotion within my heart (my spirit) without changing facial expression. I did this for what seemed an hour. Without changing facial expression (my body had dissipated into the hum along with all other surroundings), I could change what was happening behind my eyes.

Okay, I got side-tracked well actually fell asleep while writing this. It's funny how sometimes things seem important but after a while they get pushed aside for something else, like a nap.

Meditation has the ability to walk, talk, learn, just

as if I weren't in it.

In order for me to reach the next phases, I need to be in phase 1. Over the years I have learned to slip into meditation very easily to help me ground. The times I cannot enter are times when I am jealous of others, spiteful, obsessive, hateful, or resentful. Those feelings are very self-sabotaging, and only create negative outcomes for me.

Entering one of the second phases, which are several different spaces but can be entered simultaneously, I have to release the clench on the world around me. The clench of supposed to. I cannot go in wanting to fix things I actually cannot. I cannot fix how other people think, I cannot fix or control what is actually going on around me because, when I try to control these things, its actually just trying to control my mind. If I am to be the hum, everything that is going on around me is me.

I cannot fix if a chair breaks beneath me, I cannot fix if I lose a race, I cannot fix if I slip on the pool deck, or if I get stung by a bee. I cannot fix having it rain on an expected sunny day. I cannot fix the fears others face. If I were to teach myself "I'll be at peace when," or "I'll be at peace when I get the right award; I'll be at peace when I get the right grade; I'll be at peace when I get the right haircut; I'll be at peace when..." I am only setting myself up for disappointment. I can only give myself peace within my own spirit. That is why this state of being is like floating in nature.

Dear Flower Lady,

Sometimes it was all that was needed—a bit of fresh air to calm the feeling of confinement. And so it was, they lay together allowing the electricity to speak. Feeding themselves from the earth's energies, bonding without words. Disappearing into the hum.

I am ready

Dear Flower Lady,

I think trees communicate with each other. The whispering of the trees I don't think just means the wind in the branches. I think they actually have a consciousness. I remember digging around in the garden beneath the bushes and trees when I was looking for a place to mail my letters, and the roots were like a netting. I don't know why this came to mind today, but there was a lot of stuff going on, it was almost like I exposed some of their secrets. I remember feeling as though they were talking to each other and to me. I touched them softly and apologized for disrupting them. I didn't bury anything there but I did go back to say hello often.

Love, Maren

Dear Flower Lady,

Today I am writing again on DNA. The question for today touches on the development of DNA. I wonder if it is set, or can outer influences change it, and can those changes continue through the next generation as a new or clean set point? I am writing today in regard to genes.

When a baby or embryo is in the tummy, it is going through amazing programming, kind of like setting the program for a Broadway play. Behind the scenes of this program there are thousands of little details from the brush of paint to voice projections, to seating and announcements. If, let's say, one of those brush strokes is made when the painter is startled, it changes the width, length, depth, and pattern of the stroke and then it influences those strokes around it. At least the appearance of those strokes. And so goes the DNA. The slight environmental variations create small modifications during development, which imbed themselves while creating a new variation of the DNA, and then it becomes an inherited trait. Maybe it's a trait which causes the plant or animal to startle even sooner or easier. Maybe it creates a happier outlook, or greater pessimism (pessimism means negative). Because this new or altered trait continues in that life through the next reproduction it may carry on and on until an alteration occurs to lessen or increase the variant.

This could be why insanity can be carried from one to another even if the immediate environment or parent doesn't behave so, it can skip generations until triggered by an event or environmental influence. People could pick a mate to more and more influence looks and in doing so more and more people will become prettier and prettier in certain areas.

I wonder if a person who comes from a poor area and was raised in wealth and a child of privilege raised in poverty would turn out to have the same personality traits as they would have otherwise. Because people from different areas have different needs for their survival and over time those traits of survival have been influenced.

That would be interesting to know.

A fresh breeze touched the leaves above.

Pushing away thick, dark negativity.

Sun broke through,

exposing life below,

awakening the breath.

Cautiously a smile grew within,

protected by the living leather of flesh.

Circling songs invited sanguinity, lifting it.

The girl in the heart came out.

Feeling life, planting wild flowers, baking bread.

Sensing home.

Come.

A low rumble moved in the distance,

sneaking forward with great speed.

Nitrogen effect, the frozen heart, life shattered, evaporating dust.

The chest left empty.

It is not a closet when the door shuts. It is home to wondrous creatures. When the door closes the walls dissipate, all around me mountains and forests, sandy beaches and oceans, and deserts. The sky comforts my mood, it rains when I cry, and it's beautiful today.

Dear Flower Lady,

In order to find quiet, mischievousness is necessary because that is where reflection is born.

I am born.

Dear Flower Lady,

I know I am not like the others. I know I am not as smart. I know I have trouble not having a daydream mind. But I learn things in my mind. I am not lonely in my mind.

Dear Flower Lady,

I like tea with honey, and I like the rain and the sun. I like hot chocolate and fires in the fireplaces and sitting real close. I like to close my eyes and go far away.

I am also always getting into mischief, I like that too.

The sun broke through the clouds and it was glorious.
If it were always sunny, we would be blind.

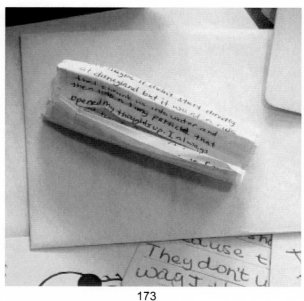

Dear Flower Lady,

Yesterday I taped the monarch chrysalises on the wall across from the window. The tape isn't actually touching the chrysalises because first I tied a thread to the little black feet that were once part of the caterpillar. They are still emerald green with beautiful gold dots. After school, I came directly to my room and shut the door. When the door shuts the world changes, the trees sway against the sky, birds fly by the window to peek in, and my physical body blends into the scenery of my antique yellow room. My spirit releases itself from the confines of the tangible.

Journals: 1985 - 1989

Swim

To stand along the swimmer's edge,

toes wrapped to brace,

The fear of water is not one that shows upon my
face.

It hurts to get my body wet,

to jump or slowly in.

For minutes, I watch the water tease,

A prism to here,

begin.

A hand upon my shoulders,

Encouraging the step.

Inside it hurts,

My skin it cries

Upon the water's depth.

Dear Flower Lady,

I bathed in the full moon all night on the roof. It was warm out, and I remembered sitting on the roof with my dad to watch fireworks a long time ago.

Solitude is joy.

Quiet resolution; a distant bird's song.

Dear Flower Lady,

Sometimes I lay in bed and wonder if I would want to meet my real mom. But I don't know. But I want to be walking down the street and meet her and she wouldn't know who I was and I would open the door for her if she was going into a door. And she would say thank you. And I would say you're welcome. And my heart would whisper her a secret.

And then I would go back to my mom and wonder if her heart whispers secrets to my brother and sisters. I hope it does.

Dear Flower Lady,

   I wish there was a way to reverse time.

   Sometimes it is a desperate feeling knowing you cannot.

Dear Flower Lady,

Today I have an observation.

I think I am a pagan.

In school, they teach us we have 5 senses, but what if that is not true. What if, what if we have more than has been measured? We are like the plants, we give off smells to signal what is happening in our personal environment, both inside and out.

Plants can think and remember, and they can communicate to the world around them.

Our bodies do the same. I've noticed the scent changes in people around me, in their breaths and from their skin (not just sweaty armpit smell).

This is what I've noticed. Did you know the breath and smell of the body of a human change according to illness, happiness, fear, and other emotions they are experiencing? So does a plant.

The sweet smells are signs to other plants and animals that things are ok. But when the plant is hurt or consumed, they not only try to heal themselves with a scab, but they let off defensive scents. Plants have defense mechanisms, poisons and thorns to try to keep predators away. They love music and soft whispers, and the gentle touch of animals (humans included). If we learn to listen through our bodies as a whole, not just our ears, we will find life. The secrets, the whispers, the communication between plant and animal.

Dear God,

I don't know what you are or if you are out there. I know you aren't a person and there isn't a place with streets lined with gold.

A real god wouldn't make that, he wouldn't make stupid promises to some parts of the world, while ignoring others.

But people need to feel connected. Sometimes they use you to feel less guilty.

I believe you are probably a part of all of us, the energy that binds the elements, weaving us together.

I know you aren't the answer to prayers, although I have prayed to you to help me not have nightmares.

Do you know what I get in return? I get to explore, to travel the universes. I get to see inside the eyes around me. I put myself in their shoes, I try to learn what makes their feelings, choices, and actions.

You know what I've learned. You are a part of it all. Because you are the connector. We are all connected.

If someone hits someone, it makes them hurt and feel bad. Then their feelings affect the next person and so on.

So, the actions of fear could actually be based from a thousand people away. But we can also plant seeds of gentleness and send them out to possibly affect a thousand people away.

Good luck to you out there

Dear Flower Lady,

There was life. Simple and beautiful. The spring awoke with the gentle song. For a moment, she stood; the daffodils dispelling the surrounding world's world. And for a moment her heart found peace.

Dear Flower Lady,

The more swimming is jammed down my throat the more my mind shuts off. It is 8 hours a day dedicated to working out or talking about exercise. The programmed exercises and swimming separates me from the natural world. There is no time to be outside, to be in the woods, to feel the earth hum through your feet.

Dear Flower Lady,

I would rather not talk.

I was a diver before I was a swimmer. I liked diving because I was the only one in the lesson and all the other kids were at swim practice. I didn't have to talk to them like I do now. In the locker room, they talked about swim practice and I would just get dressed. I still do this, but my parents think there is something wrong with me. When I try to be social they think something is wrong with me then too.

I just want to build forts, plant gardens, share flowers.

Or climb pine trees and pop sap bubbles and taste the sap and smell the breath of the tree, and feel like home.

One time I was in the car with my older sister, her friend, and her friend's mom. I was in the front seat. They were talking and it sounded just like noise. I just wanted it to be quiet. We were going to pizza. So, I just casually said, "Shit, Fuck, Damn."

The whole car got really quiet. Then the mom told me not to ever say those words again.

And the car was quiet until we got to the pizza place.

It worked like wonders if I should say so myself.

This is a story about when I was 5.

On Thursday afternoons, when the blue pushed through the Oregon mists, she and I would play in my room. We were about the same age, 5. She was very quiet, not like the other kids I knew. She never left my couch. She always looked out the window or colored in her paper book with her own pencil.

We never spoke with our mouth. It was like we heard each other's thoughts. When the sun began to set, she would somehow go home. She always waited for me to look down at my paper, or out the far window away from hers, and sneak away.

An Englishman, whose design was after his parents' manor set on one of England's country sides, had built the house 100 years earlier.

Winter began its approach to my 6th birthday, which also was its birthday, and that was the best part of that day; it being the shortest day of the year, and that the mint of candy canes brightened the dark star-studded sky.

It was a Thursday, so my friend was there. Brown wispy curls, navy cardigan over her plaid dress, with dark tights and patent leather Mary Janes.

She requested something of me this time; to find her mother.

So, I did.

"My friend wants to know where her mother is," I

asked standing next to the antique pullout stovetop in the kitchen.

"What friend?"

"My friend in my room."

"What friend in your room?"

My mother was looking at me liked I'd fallen off a turnip truck.

"You know... My coloring friend. In my room? On my couch?" She kept looking at me. "She always goes home when it starts getting dark?"

As I continued my description, my mother's face began to get pale.

"What did she want you to tell me?" My mother sat at the kitchen table.

"She just wants to know where her mom is." I scratched at my white tights.

"Let me tell you a story. A long time ago a family lived in this house, and there was a little girl about your age who was coming from school."

My friend's image flashed as if she were right before me hopping out of the car with skinny wheels and going into the mudroom by the garage.

"She'd forgotten a book in the car or something."

I knew this book I could get it. My friend was nodding excitedly; I was catching on. My mother saw my eyes acknowledging the tale as if it were happening right now.

"Only something happened when she ran out," my mother said.

My heart sank. I watched the scene before it left my mother's lips.

"Why was the car backing up?" I asked.

"I can't tell you."

"My friend went under the car?" I asked while watching my friend walk away from me, through the kitchen, through the mudroom door. The trees were smaller than they were now as they swayed in the dusk. The red paint of the big car seemed to drip from beneath the rumble seat spilling slowly around the skinny tires. My friend never came back. It was like she heard the story and that was enough.

I missed her. I wanted my friend back. I asked for her at night when the world was still, thinking the message might reach her more easily.

Dear Flower Lady,

The best way to avoid playing the violin is sitting high in a tree.

Dear Flower Lady,

I know everyone thinks I am sneaky. Mostly I just want to be alone. Today in my sneakiness I started writing notes and stuffing them on the shelves at the supermarket for people to find.

It will be like a surprise for them.

Dear Flower Lady,

It wasn't until later in the year until the gravity hit. Was it the death of the foliage? Was it the harvest? Was it the thought of a permanent hibernation? It was as though with the last leaf to fall silently to the earth that she knew, and winter stunned her heart.

Dear Flower Lady,

It started at Disneyland. Well, maybe it didn't start directly at Disneyland, but it was a ride that shrunk us into water and then into a tiny particle that my thoughts opened up. I was always reluctant of that ride because it let my mind explore just enough to want to keep going, but then the ride was done and we would go back into the regular world with the people mover gliding by, and smell of buttered popcorn on our way to the submarines. I didn't mind the submarines because you could just to sit and think, 20,000 leagues below the surface.

The transition between wanting to be alone with my thoughts and interacting with others has always been very difficult for me. It's like dropping oil in water.

The questions that would always come are, what is smaller than an atom, and how do they talk to each other? Do they use a form of echolocation? If I have DNA, does the atom have it as well? If DNA is a group of molecules, then they have to communicate in some way. Do they work like pictures or do they mirror thoughts?

I remember. I remember. I remember my mother. I remember the feeling of her laugh. I remember the bracing of her cry. She still cries sometimes, it feels like a little alarm. I didn't know what this alarm was at first, but then I started following it, and it was almost like her atoms were talking to mine. So, does that mean some of my atoms are with her? I've never met her in person.

191

I call these tiny atoms, the atom's atoms, rice. They move like dust particles in the ray of sunlight shining in from the windows. I often lay in those rays at home. The particles can hit one another, and sometimes it's like they trade secrets, they send a shadow of themselves through each other. So, does that shadow contain a shadow of their thoughts? Does that shadow continue sharing communication with its originator even if they are far apart from each other?

I think, yes.

Dear Flower Lady,

My English teacher didn't believe I was writing my own papers. I told him, "I do write them." He told me to show him right now and write 500 words about what we read in class. But there were three other girls standing around his desk listening to this conversation and I wished I'd disappeared.

"I didn't read it," I said, and the girls started snickering.

"She does the same thing in science," one of the girls said as if it needed to be stated. So, I wrote a poem story about what we did in class instead with my 500 words.

My teacher says my writing surprises him because the ideas are far more complex than what I show in ways of my school reading level (not my at home in secret level). My spelling is also very phonetic, which I am well aware of. I write one word a million times in different ways trying to remember the rules. Just look at the word laugh. I spell it as lauph. Ph sounds like an f and gh is usually silent or can sound like ew. So, the word laugh doesn't follow the rules. It's a rule exception. Like I before E, why does it matter if it's after a C or not? because there are exceptions to that rule too!

Anyway, I go to school now and hide in the bathroom stall, instead of walking as I usually do as close to the lockers so I can hopefully disappear. I stay in the bathroom until the tardy bell rings and then go to my new class. I've been going three weeks now, and I cry inside my heart for several reasons. Mostly because I am ashamed of myself for being ashamed of myself.

It is a class with the kids that are retarded and can't talk or hold a pencil. But they are just trapped in a body and they can't help it. I am ashamed of myself for feeling embarrassed but now I really know I am a dummy and so does my brother. He was even teasing about the note I left in the bathroom. So what I forgot the h in school, it sounded the same. My mom told him to be quiet. I could still hear them from my bed.

When I wrote my poem for the teacher, one of the girls told me I was so full of shit my eyes are brown.

When I went home, I looked into the mirror, into my brown eyes, and repeated the words. Then I had to go to swim practice.

Sometimes I wish I were dust. I hate swimming too.

Into the dust.

Dear Flower Lady,

I told my mom I don't want to sit next to my dad at dinner anymore.

She asked me why I would say such a thing.

There was a lady next to us at the supermarket today and she had two different shoes and two different socks and a droopy rainbow sweater.

I could feel her next to me and it made me feel weird. So, I asked my mom if I could wait next to the door for her and I bought a piece of chocolate.

And then I asked if we could have breakfast for dinner because I like it when she makes breakfast for dinner. She said no. So, I asked her maybe someday. And she said maybe someday.

We went to lunch and I was getting my salad and the lady from the supermarket came in and she sat by herself at her table. I kept looking at her. I couldn't eat my salad because I knew she was on the other side of the salad place. I even had extra beets and sunflower seeds.

It was like I was not in charge of myself and I walked to the lady's table and put my piece of chocolate by her plate and said, "I just wanted you to have this. That's all." And her eyes were teary. I could eat my salad then.

I love honey like the bees love the nectar

Greek: Sarkazein "to tear or strip the flesh off."

Why sarcasm hurts.

It is a teasing remark that someone thinks is funny but it actually hurts. It is a form of verbal abuse. Repeating snide "funny" comments hurts. It is caustic and is hardly funny. It kills my heart, but I have to pretend it is funny or the stupid person keeps going, keeps digging. The comments are real. The comments really hurt.

I am hurting inside, and find my own words bite with the pain I feel just to make people leave me alone.

Dear Flower Lady,

There are jerks in the world. People who bully. People who hurt others. There is an evil queen in Snow White. There is a wicked witch in the land of OZ. There is a Darth Vader in Star Wars. They are part of the story.

Dear flower Lady,

Quiet.

Complexity amplifies subtle graces; eloquence.

The same quiet can be mean, almost calculating; ignoring pain.

Like preparing a recipe for pies, preserves, and bread. Timing is important, and silence can be a place of powerful healing.

Because I am trapped. Because I am trapped inside my head. If I could just communicate with what is in my head rather than words. The stuff in my head is like poetry, it amazes me sometimes to hear it. It is full like the harvest moon and sprouts as the sunflower's seed. Absorbing me like the mists upon the shore, and the words sail away before I can share them.

When I swim I am not racing the other kids, I am only chasing the escape.

Dear Flower Lady,

Here is a dream I had.

Bright was the sky with a warming sun,

and through the mists is when it begun.

Dry grasses swayed, acting as fuel,

flint and steel were the main tool.

A billow of smoke was sent up above,

and soon it was cast dark like a glove.

Here it was tricky,

the sea and the coast,

as much as it tried they refused the hot roast.

The mountains however invited the flame and the
winds were right there to join in the game.

To them it was fun,

the speed and the heat.

Through the valleys they raced,

the hills—what a feat!

Weeks added up, the miles they grew.

Until one day when it was finally through.

Ashes and dust,

the wood on the ground,

the trees were quite silent,

Barely a sound.

Winter soon came,

Bringing some cold,

The ground was still parched by the stories they told.

Barren it was and soot it was blackened,

The clouds overheard and their spouts?

Well they opened.

Gently at first,

The plants were most grateful,

their colors returned

and the hills smiled

as they grew playful.

What fun this has been said the clouds to the coast,

Let's continue to water,

let's give them the most!

On it went,

the rain and the wind,

Around every tree,

it seemed that they spinned.

The grounds were so full,

They popped like a tick,

Over the roads they went heavy and thick.

People were stuck

There was no way to home,

And the rivers raged wild,

Sending north the poor gnomes.

It was here that I walked,

Quiet and calm,

Listening to the earth

Dear Flower Lady,

I think there may be a reason we cannot really see our own faces without a mirror. I believe we are not meant to focus on ourselves superficially. We are part of the canvas. When there isn't a mirror we can walk into a room and forget ourselves, but with a mirror people tend to fuss about their hair, they apologize for how they look, they worry about their clothes.

They become a thing.

Imagine if mirrors were actually windows to the landscape outside, with the earth and trees, with the lunar moths and butterflies in the apple trees, with the rains and lightning, and the sun kissing the horizon. If that is what people saw in the mirror they would feel beautiful, they would feel part of life, part of the hum.

There is a reason we don't see our own faces. Because we are already beautiful, we are already part of life.

Dear Flower Lady,

I wonder what determined life. I do not believe all Darwin said. I believe he was wrong on several accounts, but because others cannot prove otherwise they teach it like fact. Life is so much deeper. I agree in survival of the fittest, but some of his thoughts on evolution are incorrect. My guess is in about 70 years it will be challenged, there will be changes in our global environment, but not from what they are trying to tell us about an impending global ice age due to hairspray. Whatever the change is, it will alter the animal populations, the plants will change, our oceans will be practically empty of life, the Great Barrier Reef and Molokini Island's reef will be practically dead. We will find that there were more types of humanoids than we think there were. We will find out people have been around a lot longer than we think, that there was intelligence similar to what we have now, but the tools developed as resources as experimentation progressed. But I think our earth is just like us, but on a much larger scale, it goes through cycles. I know this is gross, but think about a girl having her period. The earth is the girl. The first few days of the month and she is ok, then she gets a ton of energy and can concentrate really well. Then she gets feeling sluggish and her face breaks out, then all of a sudden boys are looking cute to her, then she gets small hot flashes and then cramps and chills and then big hot flashes, and she flushes herself while wanting to go into hibernation, and she feels cold and chilly with heat waves. Then she comes out of it and it starts all over again!

So, what if she was the earth? All these changes in weather are what are supposed to happen. Monthly, seasonally, yearly, by the decade, by the century, by the millennium. I will bet my bottom dollar (if I had a dollar), that the earth has cooled down before and that it is going to heat up. It obviously got so cold we had an ice age, and before that is was so warm it was extremely tropical, we find buried extinct animals, so what makes us believe our species cannot go extinct? If hairspray is killing us and the fumes from cars are killing us (which are obviously not good for us because it can kill us), then wouldn't we be like a parasite on the planet? The earth is going to shed us just like the girl on her period the girl still lives, but the egg she had didn't. Just think of the amount of blood it takes to shed one tiny microscopic cell. That means the earth will be shedding other plants and animals to get rid of the human, at least the human as we know it. So that means, all of this stuff saying we are ruining the earth, is it right? Yes, we are just ruining it. The earth will be ok, she is just going through her cycle and she is going to shed the surface layer and start again.

Dear Flower Lady,

If I were to become a nun should I have to read the bible? Should I have to go along them in order to spend time helping people?

I am a truly selfish being and really deserve no better than the next. May my heart be humbled and my mind taught as to what love is fully.

May the days, no matter how long or short, be not wasted on greed but in the breath around my being.

Should my selfish acts hurt others, may my final days on this earth be in humility, and should those hurt by me know my meanings were not ill intent, but blinded through avoidance.

Myself created mote.

Dear Flower Lady,

    In a flash of a dream it came to me,

    the timing still unknown,

    from my arms it ripped from me,

    the greatest love I've known.

Dear Flower Lady,

　　Depth is unchanging as it is in constant motion like the sea. It moves with the storms, and stills with the calm, and can be both at the same on different shores.

　　If we are not actually solid, that means we are more of an illusion. Which means life is an illusion and we are all connected.

Dear Flower Lady,

They say insanity is seen through the color blue. That the mind finds blue stimulating enough to calm itself. When I look at blue it is one of the most complex colors. This complexity is why the color is favored, it has so many shades. One of the most famous examples of blue is through a painter called Picasso. I read he was insane because of something called schizophrenia. This condition is a broken link between thoughts, emotions, and reality. According to what was written about him, his blue period was triggered by the suicide of his friend. I would imagine, though, he was already a different thinker, and that this event caused a serious reaction within his already altered mind. Working with the blue spectrum he was able to lose his pain. It was lost to the woman with folded arms and spoke through the woman whose eye seemed blind. In those paintings you can feel him, you can feel the pure spirit who was trapped in a body and was crushed. It is not that blue is the color of insanity, but it is the color that can distract it for a moment into peace. After all, isn't that what we all seem to be after? Peace?

Dear Flower Lady,

   There it was, the hidden sun

   A mist beneath the branches

   To where the whispers of the wind

   Masked the fairies' glances

   Traces marked a wood-lined path

   Strolling the tune of nigh

   Rests a ring of toadstools though,

   Magic might imply.

Dear Flower Lady,

My poetry journal is lost. I left it under a log. I hope the person who finds it knows it was written for them. Whoever they are.

Dear Flower Lady,

Why is it that we rush to finish? We race and rush life as if it were going somewhere. But really the only place it is going is towards our always untimely death. Why don't we learn from the birds or the lounging tree frog that life is an experience to savor?

It reminds me of my dad and his stories of Vietnam. He was in hell, he doesn't talk much about the hell, but he was there. He goes around sometimes at night hiding from the enemy. Both sides in that jungle were doing what they needed to stay alive. But in hearing conversations he has when people ask him about his thoughts, he always says something that strikes a chord within me.

"When the rains came, you have never seen so much water, and when they stopped the music of the jungle came to life."

Or his tiger story—that is one of my favorites. Of course, as I got older he added that the tiger actually tripped a wire he and his platoon rigged to warn them of the Viet Cong. And they were scared and they held their breaths, as they instantly got ready to fight.

He doesn't like war. I can tell it still rages within his soul. The fear and the adrenalin and he does what he can to quiet those monsters.

That is probably why he sinks further and further into the dark spaces and has affairs, and spends money, and lashes out. He is tumbling but has nothing to hold on to so he races toward an unknown destination looking for peace.

Dear Flower Lady,

Nature's reflections of us show us the canvas, with it all. It doesn't isolate us. Nature's reflection in the water, or on a window is inclusive. It shows us we are not isolated, we are the hum.

Dear Flower Lady,

I cannot say for certain that I am heartless, but most definitely lost. I don't connect well with others as they seem to be able to. I care for them, but see life like I'm hovering above and I can zoom in. I seem to do that often too, or maybe I am just looking too close. The leaves, flowers, bugs, and birds.

The eyes and expression in movements show me things in others and I wish I could help, but I don't know how. So, I become paralyzed and don't know what to say or do. It is a helpless feeling.

Dear Flower Lady,

In many ways, wisdom comes with quiet.

Wisdom has nothing to prove to anyone. It does not lecture in halls, correct the wrong, or command attention.

Wisdom allows the world to progress; it understands our lives are part of something grander. And it understands there is meaning beyond our comprehension.

Wisdom is quiet. It is the flight of the eagle, the babbling brook, the ancient tree. It is not wielding a gun, hiding in the shadows, it is not manipulating or attacking. It is not teasing or taunting.

Wisdom is the intense division of the cell, the fluidity of molecular life; the jump of lightning, the course of the sea; the melody of the whales' song.

Dear Flower Lady,

Everyone has different skills, everyone has different understandings and they can be different because they have their way they experienced things. Even if we are all in the same place at the same time, we all experience it just a bit differently.

We all share something in common. The same thing all life shares. And that is uncertainty—the understanding that no matter how much we think we know, we actually don't know.

So, where can we find consistency? Where can we find settlement to structure? We don't. Nothing stays in place no matter how much someone wants it to. Nothing ever ends as planned. Even the earth's ground shifts. Trails and pathways crack, landscapes change, foundations alter even below our feet.

The constant we can find on a path to peace is also flexible and resides within our own bodies. This is our spirit. Our bodies are unpredictable, they are changing every moment, altering towards its demise. And we can't stop it. No matter if we work out a million hours a day or just be a bump on a log. It is still evolving like the seasons of the year.

It's ok that we don't have consistency. It's ok that our plans change. The hard part is when we start walking on the path and expect it to be there just as we planned, because when we start expecting it to be just so, then we get let down and frustrated. That's why, in the back of your mind, a plan B and C and D should be ready to step forward. Then it'll be like a junction in the train tracks and you take a detour.

Sunning on the boulder.

Dear Flower Lady,

I am sorry I don't write much anymore. I have to swim all the time and don't get to go play in the woods anymore. We wake up at 5:00 for swim practice and then go to school and then go to swim practice and then workout at home. Then if we have homework, we do homework. I do about 721 sit-ups a night when I am bored next to my bed. And then we sleep. Even on vacation we go to swim practice. Swimming is the most important thing in the world according to my dad.

I am writing because I had a dream the other night about a blue envelope. I lost it somewhere when I was little. We are moving from this house and I can't find it.

If you know where it is, can you please tell me? It was in a jar I was going to mail, but somehow it got lost. There is an important message inside.

Forgive

Dear Flower Lady,

Mostly I sit in silence. In my room. Or I lay on my floor. My heart stills and my body releases its hold. And I am free.

Dear Flower Lady,

Last night I dreamt of the images that flow in the back of my mind to the point of an almost hypnotic distraction. I can't really describe what I am seeing.

I am 13 years old now. I am a competitive swimmer and have been in special programs in school for kids that are below average. I do not communicate well because the images in my mind move fluidly compared to what is happening in the classrooms. They move much faster than I am able to write. I used to believe I was crazy. Perhaps I am.

The following theory is on the connection of all material, not only on earth, but also in space. It also touches on the idea there are webs we cannot see but are part of.

We are like the earth, which is smaller than the atom, which is like the universe.

Let's begin with our own electrical system, with the power plant being the heart. There is an electromagnetic current that domes and loops around us.

The energy created in this field is a living breathing movement that allows for connection to others. A sixth sense of feeling.

This theory is about connection.

You can actually read people from over 50 meters or more away, just by the energy being produced by their field. The closer they get, the more your senses pick up on the intention in the air.

The spheres connect and communicate with one another.

In the world of molecules, they teach us the photons and electrons move randomly around the atom. But this is only true when they are secluded from all other matter. But they do not do this in nature. They actually emulate the pattern of the element they are around and can weave two elements together even if they are for different things by creating a pattern of movements that musically (I say that because of the waves they weave are beautiful in my mind) weave the two things together. Can they connect more than two things? Yes. Most definitely.

So, by knowing this and knowing our power plant creates a sphere of energy that expands practically indefinitely, like a wave of water when a pebble is dropped in (our body is the pebble and the sphere, not only moves from our "head" looping to our "toes," waves outward weaving with everything around us.) Plants, animals, people, the earth, the air, the unseen world around us, and even [throughout] space are all connecting and communicating in some way. The most sensitive physical sensation for us is the closer something gets to our body.

My theory is we are all connected, our moods, our understandings, our worlds can be influenced by the energies being produced in our vicinity.

We are all based off the same secret codes. The entire world around us is based off the same design. We can understand a lot if we learn to realize this.

When we first got a microwave a few years ago, you could feel the strange energy coming out of it. From across the kitchen, and if you moved to stand and look inside, you could feel your mind tingling (well I felt that way anyway.) The energy acted like a strange magnet, pulling and re-arranging the atoms, it wasn't a normal harmony. It was almost hypnotizing and you wanted to move away, but it drew you in, fizzing a little like pop rocks.

This is why we get the sensation that someone is watching us from behind. It is the innate senses animals use in the wild to stalk, or to feel when it is being stalked. It is why the birds know when a storm is coming before the skies darken. It is when you can feel love from miles away. And it is why some people believe there is life after death, because although they cannot see the energy fields of the souls, they can still feel them, or smell them, or sometimes hear them.

It is why when someone dies they can haunt, because their spiritual waves are alive and they can still use them to communicate. They have a conscience.

Think about that for a moment. Words are a vibration created with a tool called a voice box. But the words are not seen, they are part of the wave.

Back to the sphere of emotional energy, does this

weaving mean that our feelings can actually influence the world? If people were to work in harmony, if they were to let go of negative feelings and embrace compassion and gratitude (even for the foods we eat), would that impact the world around us in a positive manner?

Well, I need to go. Thank you for listening.

I believe in more. I really do.

Dear Flower Lady,

Let's go back to the world of colors. Purple.

This is my purple book. I am writing in purple. But can you really see it or is it just another color of blue?

Orange is a whole color as is green, yellow, red and blue. Purple on the other hand isn't. We can't really see a pure purple not even on the rainbow shimmering on my wall. Maybe purple is like the highest note or the deepest tone. It is there but we can't see it. It is invisible to us.

Isaac Newton did experiments with prisms to break the white light into pieces using a ray of sunlight shining through a piece of crystal.

White isn't even a true color either, if you are painting with white you are painting with no color. If you are talking about white light, it is actually all the colors not broken yet through the prisms.

Purple is like life. It is an optical illusion.

Growing up is so awkward. It feels like my joints are all wiggly. Like my thoughts don't fit with my body.

I feel like Goofy.

It's like growing up is all mixed up. Like there is a bad picture on the etch-a-sketch and no matter how much you shake it, it just gets more confusing but won't clear.

Then I have to swim.

Dear Flower Lady,

Does medicine interfere with the natural life cycle? Does that in turn interfere with the health of the global well-being?

Another person has cancer, leukemia. He is only a year older than me. The last round of chemotherapy didn't work and he is going to die.

No one wants to die, really. And others don't want to endure the pain of loss. But what is it they are actually avoiding? The pain of loss, yes, but mostly the fear of mortality.

We seem to push death under a blanket so no one has to come near it until "the owl calls your name." Everything is sugar-coated to paint a pretty picture of normality. If someone dies, it's like a wet blanket on the whole parade, "You'll get over it," or "You'll move on, don't worry."

What does that even mean, "You'll get through this."

Our culture is really mixed up. A death is just as important as a birth. It is the birth for the person who dies.

There is nothing nice or easy about birth. It is exceedingly traumatic for the infant. They are being ripped from one world into another. Look at the energy in the division of a cell. That is a spectacular event. The difference between birth and death is, in birth we witness the soul entering and in death we witness the soul's exit into another "world" or state of being. Like the mother giving birth, it is excruciatingly painful, so is the death. We celebrate the birth. We hide from the death. But in death there are memories and lessons, and experiences to be held.

By extending human life we are encouraging over population, which will strain our environments as more resources will be needed to sustain life. But not just life, to sustain a quality of life.

That means, in order to live a "good" life, we are told it's got to have certain qualities. The house, the clothes, the car, the shampoo, the zit cream, the potato chips, the vacations, and the education. We are told we must acquire these things to be fulfilled and happy. But what is the truth?

It is an economic empire. It is all about money. The more people live the more they need.

In my short time in this life, I have noticed things aren't the same as I remember them when I was young. Things feel different, not so solid. Maybe it is my imagination, but I have even heard my parents say things aren't made like they used to be.

Don't get me wrong, I am not averse to advances in medicine and science. I like the exploration and think it would be fun to be a part of, but I do not like the carelessness of greed.

The case of the matter is, companies and advertisers pretend quality. More and more things are being replaced more often. Even Mickey Mouse has changed to be "cooler." Instead of sharing the magic of being yourself, Disney is moving into a popularity contest and it feels like a huge disappointment. And it's all for money and the stock price.

I did tell my dad every year, since the stock dropped a few years ago, to invest in Disney for me. Because popularity sells, lots of people want to be part of the "in" crowd.

To reduce the life of an item makes them more disposable and generates more money for the companies. To make and produce all this stuff means our resources are going to be stripped at increasing rates. It's the 1980s for goodness sakes and we are setting ourselves up for trouble. What is our world going to look like in 50 years? It's not that the earth is going anywhere, nature will be ok (it doesn't pretend there is a way out of death, it embraces it,) but we are just writing humanity's ticket out of the playbook.

Extending human life is an economy of its own. A lot of money is going into vanity and finding the fountain of youth. People or companies will create new medicines to try to heal everything. But this is bad.

If we continue extending the lifespan, and we keep making things to make lives easier and more convenient, we are going to end up in a world where we have a bunch of people with nothing to do.

Boredom creates problems on a large scale in

populations. Some individuals create ingenuity or find solace in art. The question is for the grand population, is it better to live smaller fuller lives, or longer more superficial ones?

Of course, in the end it won't matter what we do or how we live because nature will decide.

The overuse of resources will hurt our environments. What will that effect be in 10 years? Probably nothing. But what about 50 years? Will we be able to breathe? Going into LA we can see the color of the air is different. Is that brown air going to hang over everywhere? Are we going to be like the Lorax story? Will diseases like cancer increase?

Delve beyond the cell, find the other side of darkness.

Dear Flower Lady,

The path less traveled. No matter what path you are on, look around you because there is so much more. Life is not a line or a path. There is no starting line and no red tape finish. It is multidimensional...it is a phase, like the seasons. We are in the human phase and we will continue into more seasons and possibly circle back.

Dear Flower Lady,

Meander. Wander. Dilly Dally. This is me. My goals and ambitions are my desires and drives. I do not desire a path to the end. My ambition is to meander, to explore the meadow and forests of life. If I were to be a doctor, I'd bring a flower for each of my patients to bring home. If I were a teacher I would hide little things for the kids to search for. If I were a mother, there would be magic.

Dear Flower Lady,

What does it mean to love yourself? How do you do it? Always you hear people say you must love yourself to be loved. I think about this often and wonder if I am able to love myself, or if by doing so I get lost in myself.

So, how do you love yourself?

Mirror the touch of rain on a daisy, the rush of wind across a puddle.

Dear Flower Lady,

I dreamt again last night. I can imagine him as a baby in my arms, building forts as a child, but never as an adult. He just goes away and the meadow above the ocean blends over the story, and the birds sing.

Dear Flower Lady,

Boundless within the walls of plated calcium, the puzzled bone,

Synapses of electricity spark its own universe to life.

Worlds created by gentle rhythm; unmeasured time.

Complex in development, simple in structure, the stories come.

One mind alone is limited to its own existence, suppressing knowledge.

Hindering discovery.

Importance.

The universe isn't measured in miles or time except for tangible tools.

Calculated estimates.

Formulas solve the needed or desired.

Forcing the vast into a box; calling it outside.

The far reaches can be accessed instantaneously; the synapse.

The making of the universe is the making of the mind. It is the same.

She smiled; flashing now on the left; swirling galaxies, distant sparks.

Knowledge unbound.

She left with synapse.

Jumping.

The mind is grey again.

Simple.

A return to collective life.

I want to go exploring.

Less than a blink of an eye.

There and back, billions of years, measured time, vast within the puzzled walls of bone.

Dear Flower Lady,

The dream

There is something dark lurking in the shadows. A foretelling.

In the garden maze next to the roses I played in my dream. The sun set and I was in my room, beneath the covers.

From the woods at the far edge of the maze emerged a being I cannot describe other than death, and beside that shadow a head.

At first, it wasn't scary, but as it glided down the row of hedges to the French door, into the library, its darkness became prevalent. It was a warning of death.

A warning I cannot stop.

The death will be instant, but not my own, but it will feel as though it was.

A part of me will die in a setting sun. Desperate.

The beings focus on me as they make their way through the maze.

"You cannot alter the path no matter what you do. The fate is set."

Patience.

The panic started rising.

I awoke frozen. And then got out of bed and went

downstairs, skirting the hallway to my parents' room.

They were asleep. I didn't wake them. I just stared with my heart begging one of them to wake up and comfort me.

Then I went back upstairs, I decided I will change fate. I will change this path so this tragedy doesn't happen.

But what is it?

A body without a head

A head without a body

A spirit that's part of me

Dear Flower Lady,

How do you find happiness? My mother reads books about raising kids and about happiness. My dad listens to motivational tapes and talks to help build better business relationships. There was a book I snuck from his library, "How to Influence People and Win Friends."

It is an interesting title or subject line.

Do we really need to win friends? Is friendship a competition? About influencing others, isn't that the same as manipulation?

You know from my previous notes that we are merely a form of spirit or conscience essence unique and individual as the snowflake. Our views and understandings of life vary from person to person as each view is felt from an angle no one else could ever see. Therefore, reality is truly in the "eyes" of the beholder.

But what is the individual reality? And how can others influence it?

Our individual self rarely trusts our own instincts it seems. We have a need to feel guided. It is a way we survive as a species. We follow what has worked for others to thrive and to hopefully avoid catastrophe.

Good luck verses bad luck. Is a rabbit's foot good luck or bad luck? I guess if you were to ask the rabbit it wouldn't be so good, but for the starving person who caught the rabbit it was a lifesaver.

These books are kind of like the rabbit's foot books.

In order to influence others and win friends someone else is being skinned.

By playing on the doubts of mind, the master influencer (the author or speaker) leads a group towards the light of the "path less traveled." The influencer, all the while, winning a bounty of so called friends. Each friend at that point means money and meals, per say.

The followers need to have influencers as a gauge to compare themselves to. Getting the viewpoints of others to gain validation for their thoughts, accomplishments, and even failures.

This stems from a low personal value. This is interesting, because the person seeking validation or constant second opinions on things is giving value to the "gauge" or influencer.

This is seen at school with the popular group of kids. Many kids want to be like them. They try to wear similar clothes, or may even start to pick on others to prove their own value to the group.

Sometimes the seeker catches on to what is happening and begins to morph into a gauge and they find the power to influence and therefore "win" friends.

But what happens if we want real friendships? I think it would be best to say a real friendship isn't in mass quantity, but in quality. And it builds and develops over time. Sometimes people don't even get real friend until later, or maybe never.

I am sad for my dad that he thinks these tapes and books are going to make him a better salesman or person. When all he has to do is remember what it was like to fly kites so long ago on the beach.

Dear Dad,

I love you

Please be alright

Love,
maren

Dear Flower Lady,

As the sun begins to set and the hum settles the day, I pack my bags. I am not sure where I am going or what the future holds, but it is time for me to leave. I do not belong here, I don't belong anywhere really. I am scared. But I believe.

This is the last page of purple.

The pages no one can see;

Beyond the spectrum of color

Where our spirits become again free.

May there be love.

May there be hope.

May the future beyond blend,

A kaleidoscope

Where learning is knowledge,

And materialism is left,

Where the universe opens

And our souls explore a beautiful depth.

Dear Flower Lady,

You can't find salvation by looking for it from someone else. The only one that can ultimately help you is you. You are you. You are the hum. You are everything and nothing all at once. Don't worry so much about the what you should do or be, and just be the wind, be the sun upon your shoulder, the rain on your brow, and the mud between your toes.

A pencil without an eraser still writes.

And then it should read.

Choose your words wisely.

Dear Flower Lady,

Today we will be talking about universal fabrics and binding points. Imagine a swath of cotton linen. At first you see a flat surface with maybe a few irregularities. If you look closer what you find is a weave of irregular strands. Each intersection is a binding point, a form of unity.

Look closely at your skin. You will see a weave, even on very young skin. The fibers of your skin are weaving together, bonding. Inside this bonding you have cellular structure, molecules, and atoms that move with life.

Imagine each point of the linen where the strands cross. On one side of this cross is a black hole and the other side is an explosion. Material is taken in. Compressed, material is basically turned inside out if it is compressed so greatly. On the black hole side, people might think the matter turns into something negative or might cease to exist. On a super basic level it would be like the number scale where 3, 2, 1 are the black hole side, the 0 vortex where the compression is so great it forces the material into the next universal plane and the -1, -2, -3 (could quite possibly be an inverse of material) starts another complete universe. The black hole side now has a mirror or opposite plane with a reverse spin shooting material with physical laws we cannot account for here on earth. Each occurrence of the fabric's weave creates differences.

The binding points are interesting because it bind

it all together. It binds us and everything together. It is the hum. We are the hum.

You are what you project in your heart.

Dear Flower Lady,

Animals know. Their understanding of life, its meaning, and what is next is superior to ours. We are constantly looking for reasons. The reasons we are here. To place meaning and mortal facts upon it all. To break down what love is to its base. To remove one's self from nature and place our manmade religions and our sciences on a pedestal, making us actually less of an emotional group; to remove sensitivity, and become fixers.

This is where intellect become ignorance. We can break it all down, all the way through our electrical workings. Maybe someday we will construct a human outside of a human. Maybe we'll make memory outside a human, we will forge emotions in a robot. But no matter what, we will not understand the cause of emotion from inside a laboratory. Of course, a plausible explanation of what emotion is, and explain it away as reflex or a means to survival. It will miss what's behind the eyes, though, and will further restrict the spirit, creating an environment void of authentic connection. People will interact without connection. Connection is hard, it is vulnerable and can hurt.

Take a moment and do not speak.

Stay still.

Hear your breath.

Hear your heart.

Lay outside and do the same. No matter the weather.

Listen for your heart. Keep going deeper and deeper.

You'll find an expanse.

How do humans know what intelligence is? They cannot truly communicate with other beings on earth.

Because we can talk, because we can build, because we can make things like machines? That is the measure of intellect? Because we are the only creatures to make music and art?

Animals know how to play and love and how to be sad and mad and happy and glad, and how to make art. I have heard it.

I have a record of the humpback's song and of the blue whale too. I venture to say they live within art and music. Their lives are grace, they live within science, and within natural religion. They communicate through song. They teach, love, protect, care for their children and families. They attack bullies when needed.

Imagine if we lived within art and we spoke soothingly through song to one another. Anger through these melodies wouldn't create hate.

How does a dolphin or seal know to avoid explosives or warn us about them, without being trained? Why do they know it is dangerous?

We base intellect and understanding on our own skills and developments. Yet, we cannot know what another person is thinking. People have no idea how I think. When I try to explain, I am sometimes completely disregarded or humored—mostly just shut down. And I feel a fool.

Yes, of course we have all ranges of minds. Some are very simplistic and others more complex. Some with the ability to memorize a great deal and some content in a field of clovers or living in the present. They are all important. All types and stages of the mind.

How big is the whale's brain? How does it compare to the ratio for intelligence we use to compare the rat's brain or the pig's brain or to the ape's brain? I bet it dwarfs our ratio.

The sperm whale isn't silent. Some people say it is. Some people say it clicks. The clicks are in a language that is different than the humpbacks, just as French is to English, but they know them all.

Intelligence is individual to the species.

The human is a manipulative beast. Through our words we weave power. We think we thrive on controversy, on destruction, on war. Our technology started out as one thing, a discovery that could be positive, but it quickly turns into tools to advance positions or to be destructive and used as a weapon, per say. It seems everything is always fighting.

We fight disease. A car fights distance. Religion fights love. Science fights compassion. We fight each other. We gossip, we look for the wrong, we place blame and faults rather than learning everything is natural.

Not speaking properly is natural. Getting something wrong is natural. Perfection is not. Perfection is fighting nature. Perfection is fighting one's self. Perfection is the refusal to let yourself be part of nature. To know you are not, nor ever will be in control. Perfectionism is fear and self-sabotaging. Perfection is finding fault in life, it is manipulating yourself, it is fighting harmony.

For a moment, think of a rabid animal. Foaming at the mouth, vicious, and unable to remain calm. It is in panic mode. It is in pain and is very sick. It kills frantically.

The human is rabid. It destroys its own environment. It is working to extend life which could lead to unsustainable growth and over population. Humans are fighting nature.

What other creature intentionally poisons its own water and food, for perfectionism? What other animal kills just to kill like what we did to the buffalos and different races of humans, over fishing the waters, killing things to practically extinction? Over hunting, over poisoning, over reaching.

I used to wonder why spiders and snakes had enough venom to kill humans when they only eat bugs or rabbits (generically thinking). But look at the intelligent human. We kill everything in our path. We stick animals in laboratories, we mount them on our walls, strip them of their horns and tusks. All so we can be stimulated. Maybe the lessons here are to learn to let go of those traits, to live within our environment and for our environment. Maybe we return to our communities and stop fighting for oil and resources so far away—taking them from other communities. Maybe we should allow for natural population and development.

The human population lives in fear. And like the rabid dog it is in a panic for survival.

Science can be beautiful, it doesn't have to be fighting something. It can be wondrous and inquisitive.

There is more after this life, and we should learn to look through wondrous eyes, where the flower speaks silently to us and death is not so permanent. I don't want to die thinking there is nothing more, while at the same time I don't want to die thinking there are streets made of gold. I want to believe the next phase is enveloping, where the mistakes and manipulations I will make here will be translated into compassion, to eternal love, a love so true it cannot be documented.

The first time I heard the whales' song I was in Maui. My dad and I had swum out past the breakers and sunk to hover around 12 feet below the surface. The first few seconds I acclimated to the water's tide, relaxing my chest and allowed the beat of my heart to slow. It was a silence beneath the water, an untold story. Possibly the same un-silence you'd hear in space. Then it came. A beautiful voice. It was more than a song. It was poetry, an ethereal wisdom.

Each year we go back, I look forward to listening. It is me under the waves, outside my natural habitats, unobtrusive and curious. The songs fill my soul and it is like witnessing a magnificent secret.

The songs aren't only from one whale but a multiple. It is a harmonious dialog based in grace and understanding. It is a song which resonates life.

We may ... (writing here is illegible due to water)

Continued...

Imagine the whales' song as simultaneous ideas and thoughts and feelings, like Mozart, Vivaldi, Michelangelo and Aristotle all rolled into a single note.

If I could communicate like the whale, the song would fill my soul.

... (writing here is illegible due to water) Continued...

Dear Flower Lady,

Whether we want to admit it or not, there is a world beyond our tangible reality.

ccxlix

Dear Flower Lady,

What makes a meadow beautiful? Or a field of clovers grand? There is no beauty in perfection, only heartache and hardship. Perfection suits no purpose but to push away love. To love is to see the meadow and the clovers, with the dandelions and thistles, not to brag, boast, compare or blame.

To love is to have faith for it is intangible, unmaterialistic, it is a connection to the unseen.

Dear Flower Lady,

First, I would like to make note of the perforations on the pages of this notebook. Should you like to remove any pages, you may tear them out. But it is important to remember that even though the pages are removed from this book, the words remain printed for eternity in a form of special memory.

What is this form of special memory you ask? Consider this:

Space isn't empty. There is something so tiny, so tiny it continues beyond anything the future can measure. This "tiny" is the essence, it is living. It is the essence of life. It is what fills the spaces, however large or small, that scientists claim as empty. If you think about atoms for a moment, an atom lives as both a matter and a wave. You may be scratching your head, but please bear with me. What I am referring to is atomic consciousness. When no one is looking, it spreads out kinda like a liquid. But when it is looked at it condenses. It has its own sense of self. It only appears in a particular place if you measure it (kind of like time). It is an observer that makes matter known, and if you really think about it, the act of observation creates the entire universe. But in that observation, is it the human body that is the observer or does the human body act as a tool for the essence of life? This makes the essence of being an untouchable reality; meaning an external being; the individual spirit.

Dear Flower Lady,

There once was a little boy who tripped over his shoelaces and skinned his knees. Rocks and dirt that ground into them were picked out carefully by his little fingers. Tears stung the corner of his eyes. Sometimes kids laughed at his misfortune.

He stood up and barely made his way home, his head held high so it could cover the pain and fear of embarrassment. Over the years he learned to become a great mason. His structures were beautiful to behold. People were in awe, some wanted to stay watching the master work. They set out picnic blankets and offered for him to join them. But still he worked. He hand-carved the bricks, stacked each stone, and tended the grounds until they were just so.

Bandits and looters and even lovers battered the heavy doors. He looked out the windows to take quick glances at the commotions. Sometimes he'd miss a brick (or twenty) and in his negligence the invaders snuck in. He pushed them out quickly, though, and got back to work.

The weather and time were not his friend, as much as he'd hoped they would be. They were sunny and bright when he was working, but chipped away everywhere his back was turned. He became exhausted. The walls began crumbling stones into dust. He built up the fires and packed mud into the holes. He held his head as high as he could. It was a lonely job striving for perfection, all this work for barren walls; sterile art perfectly placed.

Dear Flower Lady,

Thank you for listening.

Love, Maren

Dear flower lady,
I really am trying to write
straighter. I put the lines behind
the paper today so they won't
be all over the page.

Maren
r r r r r r r Maren
Maren

Once upon a time a long
time ago my dad took
us sledding in the
newly fallen snow.
The road were the
ice like a shimmering
black sky where the
tobgin's narrow blades
are fast enough to fly.

Made in United States
North Haven, CT
10 November 2021